MW00618265

"Tara Whitney's strategy ~~for rejecting society's ingrained~~ thin ideal is the perfect antidote to feelings of shame, distrust, and the 'wrongness' we as women feel in our bodies. This is a fresh perspective on acceptance of body and self. If you play the "When I ... Then I..." game, (when I fit in that dress then I will apply for that job) this book is for you. Tara also shares simple (but not easy) exercises to get the reader more in touch and in tune with their 'here and now' bodies. Thank you, Tara, for sharing your truth and justifying the feelings of so many around cultural norms."

—ANNE POIRIER, author of *The Body Joyful, My journey from self-loathing to self-acceptance*, Founder of Shaping Perspectives, A Woman's Way to Joy, www.shapingperspectives.com

"I wish every woman in the world could read this book! Tara provides a blueprint for leading healthier, happier lives. Her insight and wisdom are invaluable. The world needs *Truly Seen!*"

—MARIA SCRIMENTI, Certified Intuitive Eating Counselor, www.mariascrimenti.com

"This book is a must-read for anyone who craves an honest discussion about the heartache of perfectionism. Tara shares her own story of striving and dieting and invites readers to awaken to the illusion of 'the promise of the thin and perfect' that women are born into. She bravely decodes this "promise" and compassionately shows the way to break free."

"Three words came to me as I read this book; vulnerable, revealing, and inspiring. Tara not only walks you through the journey of how we get stuck in hiding, she also provides expert advice on how to overcome it. If your body image has ever left you feeling like you have to hide or has ever gotten in the way of getting what you want in life, then this is the book for you."

"Tara Whitney does an excellent job of illustrating the price we pay for the illusion of perfection and belonging. Reading *Truly Seen*, I felt seen, understood, and comforted in the pain of navigating our oppressive cultural roles as a woman leader. If you have ever felt like you needed to be someone better, this book is for you. Not only will you finally feel seen, you will also be empowered to break the cycle."

TRULY
SEEN

STOP STRIVING TO BE
THIN AND PERFECT
AND SET YOURSELF FREE

TARA WHITNEY

Published by Birch Tree Press

Book design and production: Domini Dragoone – Sage Folio Creative
Editors: Amy Isaman, Christina Roth, Maggie van Galen, Holly Tomilson
Photo of author: Sunshine White

Library of Congress Cataloging-in-Publication Data

ISBN: 978-1-7339096-2-4 (paperback)
ISBN: 978-1-7339096-3-1 (e-book)

Printed in the United States of America

For Mark, Ryan, Garrett and Anna.

*You've shown me what it means to
be truly seen. I love you.*

CONTENTS

TRULY
SEEN

INTRODUCTION

I was eight the day my mother told me about my biological father. Like, still riding my light blue Huffy bike with its cushy seat and streamers coming from the handlebars, spinning cartwheels and playing on our neighbor's jungle gym (we didn't have our own). Until that moment, I never questioned why my last name was her maiden name. It just was. I didn't think anything was wrong.

My mother asked me to sit with her at the round table, tucked neatly in the corner of our small kitchen. Her voice was soft and she delivered each word slowly, which was unlike the clear, loud voice that made her such a good cheerleader in high school. I could tell that what she had to say was going to be important. She told me my biological father's name and that they weren't in a position to get married. That was enough for me—

I couldn't hold in this super-duper secret. This news made me feel special, something that set me apart from the other kids I knew. I ran up the street to my best friend Heather's house and told her.

The excitement didn't last long, though, and the novelty quickly wore off. The older I got, the more questions I was asked about my different last name. I responded simply, "My mother didn't marry my biological father." I always got the same reply: "Oh." or "Hmm." No further questions. It stopped the curious in their tracks. There was no acknowledgment of understanding. They could have said, "Oh, my friend from church doesn't know his biological father, either." But I understood their silence. We both knew something was unusual—that something was *wrong*—with how I came into this world. My difference made me an outcast.

When my hair started to get curly during puberty, my mother would tell me it reminded her of Uncle Bob, my one uncle with big, bushy hair that would look wild when he took his football helmet off. But I couldn't get a comb through my unruly curls so I suspected my curls didn't come from him. And when my aunts would drink coffee and smoke cigarettes in my grandmother's kitchen, the signature family nose would come up—who had one and who didn't. I'd look in the mirror at my nose. It didn't look like theirs. I wasn't sure whose it looked like.

When I was in college, I needed a passport so I could travel abroad for a semester. I left the father's date of birth and birthplace blank on the application because I only knew his name. The reaction of the woman behind the desk at the passport center stunned me. "What? You don't know? We need this information!" How could I give her information I didn't have? I left in tears. And worried that I wouldn't get a passport so I could travel. I worried that this was a punishment I inherited and couldn't do a damn thing about.

Even though I had no control over the circumstances of my birth, I still felt shame around it. I knew what it was like to be an outsider. I knew I was loved by my mother, brother, and grandmother. There was no question about that. Knowing you're loved and knowing you belong, however, are two different things. When you don't belong, you need to be someone who can fit in and be accepted.

Shame thrives in the darkness. When we feel like we don't belong, we can't show the part of us that's wrong and broken. No one witnessed me as a young child with a different last name feeling like an outsider in her own home. No one knew or understood how important it was to spend endless hours trying to straighten my curls that refused to comply, no matter how hot the curling iron and how strong the Aqua Net.

I now share my story knowing I was never broken to begin with. But while that shame lived deeply inside of me, I was determined to prove myself worthy of belonging, which meant I needed to show the world the best version of me that I could. I quickly got a taste of the high that comes from feeling good enough. I would bask in praise when I hit a home run on the softball field, scored a goal on the soccer field, or earned my place on the dean's list in college. Yes, I could stand in the light. But only when I was perfect.

Perfection wasn't just about my accomplishments; it was also about how my body looked. When I was growing up, my grandmother told me I had "big bones." This may have just been a casual observation to her, like saying "It's bitter cold outside," or "This soup needs salt." But to me, she was telling me my body wasn't right. And she wasn't the only person I learned that from. I knew big bones weren't pretty because the popular girls at school were thin and cute. When I saw my mother avoid birthday cake and pasta, she was showing me how I could make my body smaller, too.

In many ways, trying to be thin and perfect saved me. We all get the formula for success at a very young age. We understand what it takes to rise above, get noticed, stand out, and excel in life. When following this formula, it can feel like we are in control of our lives.

And in my case, and likely yours as well, we try to control the uncontrollable. When you don't belong and feel alone, you'll do whatever it takes to show the world that you're worthy. Striving to be perfect and to have a thin, attractive body was a lifeline, one I gladly grasped onto.

These two things walked hand in hand—being a perfect, acceptable, worthy version of myself and being as thin as I could be. I wouldn't be happy with one and not the other. So I spent decades mending my "brokenness" by pursuing both. It became normal. Working hard, skipping meals, going on long runs. It was benign. In fact, my work ethic was often praised. People would say, "You're so disciplined," "You're so diligent," "You're so strong." But really, this is who I had to be. I didn't know any other way. I didn't have a choice. Until I understood I could choose differently.

I started to realize that I was paying a huge price by being this way. I was exhausted. No matter how hard I tried, it was never enough. I was constantly trying to figure out how I could eat the right thing, not let anyone down, accomplish all that was expected of me, and still get myself out the door in the predawn hours for a long run so I could keep my weight down. So much effort with very little reward. I'm going to share more about this reckoning and awakening in the chapters that follow.

Understanding the influence cultural ideals have on women was a critical piece for me. I internalized these ideals and made them my own. I asked myself: *What's wrong with me? Why can't I do this right? Why can't I be more disciplined?* This is what destructive cultural narratives do; they place blame and shame on the individual. When I saw clearly how these cultural systems were created, who benefited from them and who didn't, and the impact they had on women both individually and as a collective group, I knew this mechanism needed to be named. It needed to be called out so you could point to it and say, "It's not me, it's this." and feel tangible relief knowing you've done nothing wrong. You've just been trying to survive in a world where you feel like you don't belong and you've been given a harmful strategy to prove your worthiness. I call this mechanism the Promise of the Thin and Perfect, and you'll find out pretty quickly why it's so harmful.

I started to navigate a new way to live in this world. A way without trying to make my body thin and proving that I was good enough. I practiced sitting with myself and seeing my own value. Not a value that comes from the outside which needed to be earned, but one that I knew existed just because I'm walking here on earth. I started to experience a freedom I didn't know was possible. I'm still uncovering this personal sovereignty, and I know it will be more and more expansive with time.

As I connected the dots between the pursuit of thinness and perfectionism, the vision for my life's work and who I was meant to serve became crystal clear: I saw armies of women, millions of beautiful minds and hearts being sedated and kept under a spell, purposely being distracted from their lives to fight a nonexistent cause. Women who possess great wisdom and brilliance, yet walk around in a trance, not being able to express themselves, share their wisdom, create what's in their heart and soul, and share themselves fully with those they love. Women who want to love deeply and share their passions with the world. Women who want better for their children and better for their parents. Women who just want to relax but are so willing to work tirelessly to make the world a better place. Women who have so much energy that they could power the sun but instead are tired and frustrated. Women who just want to be free yet are stuck, spending hours upon hours, years upon years trying to move themselves forward only to be exhausted and exasperated. Women who believe they've been doing the right thing, thanks to a culture that has been cheering them on, deceiving them, and convincing them to not give up. But really, they are fighting a losing battle.

I was also a soldier in this army. It's for this army and for you, warrior, that I write this book. Our time is precious. Your energy is priceless. You've been wasting it ... and you've been suspecting this is the case. If your pursuit of perfection and thinness was working for you, don't you think you would have achieved it by now? But it hasn't and it won't.

When you share your brilliance with the world, you are willing to be fully witnessed just as you are, without any conditions, promises, or hopes of change. It's raw and freeing. It's a journey. A switch doesn't get flipped. Navigating this journey requires you to undo all the false beliefs, assumptions, and expectations you've accumulated in order to uncover what's underneath. Experiencing your value, not as a condition someone else has defined for you, but instead as a universal truth. A truth that's been there the whole time, but you don't know how to live with it.

You need to know what I now know. You need to wake up each day and not feel bound to trying to lose weight and trying to live up to an ideal that someone else created for you. I know you've been believing these are worthwhile endeavors, because I certainly did. In the pages that follow, I'll explain to you what these worthless endeavors are so you can see them for yourself.

I'm writing this book from my cisgender, able-bodied, average-weight, heterosexual, middle-aged, white, female experience. I acknowledge the privilege I've experienced as a result of being born with traits allowing me access to what others don't. This privilege includes, but is certainly not limited to, access to education, healthcare, workplace advancement, home financing, clean water, and safe communities. The stories and practices I offer come from my lived experience and those of my clients, whose identities are similar to mine. If you live without any of these identities, you live with greater vulnerability and risk. You may require additional support and resources to move through your journey. My hope is that by recognizing my privilege, you can recognize your own need for support, visibility, and resources.

I know I'm not alone with an origin story of feeling like I don't belong. Enough women have shared with me their unique stories, and how they concluded the same thing I had. I can see clearly what's happening. We are just trying to make ourselves whole again. But our patriarchal culture, the one that dismisses and devalues women, holds embedded harmful ideals around thinness and perfection. We've agreed to pursue these ideals without even realizing we have another choice. Our path to wholeness, when absorbed with and committed to fulfilling these ideals, only leaves us feeling more broken and disconnected.

Welcome, my friend. I see you. I witness your struggles. In this book, I'll share mine. I know you've been doing all you can to feel like you are acceptable and belong. But engaging in the strategies we've been given from a culture that demands our perfection doesn't serve us; it only harms us. I'm about to tell you what these strategies are and why they hurt so damn much. I'm going to share with you why you've been believing this pursuit of perfection has been the only option and why you've been so dedicated to this endeavor. I'm going to share with you what the real impact has been so you don't feel crazy and blame yourself any longer. I'm going to give you the tools and practices to break free from this bind so you can reclaim precious time and energy and feel successful and happy right now. Just as you are. And I'm going to offer you a path forward, one on which you can share your unique brilliance.

You want what I want. To be in this world, to uncover your brilliant self so your light can shine so freakin' bright. I'm going to share with you how to be truly seen.

CHAPTER 1

WHEN YOU'RE THIN AND PERFECT

In the fall of 2019, I joined a few hundred accountants to honor a handful of women leaders in the profession at a luncheon, held at one of Boston's prestigious waterfront hotels. Seeing that sea of women accountants felt familiar and foreign at the same time, as if I was returning to my childhood home. For one, the profession had changed. The industry was now focusing on attracting and maintaining women. I had also changed; I was still a Certified Public Accountant, but had become a full-time body image coach, too.

This wasn't my first time attending an event with a large group of professionals. However, it was the first time I had ever seen women leaders be publicly recognized. I was curious. Besides needing some professional education credits, I wanted to offer my former CPA sisterhood solidarity.

The emcee was ready for the stage, wearing impeccable makeup and high heels. She introduced each woman leader one by one, asking them to sit on the stage in large, comfy chairs. Like thrones. The emcee shared why each woman was being nominated as an outstanding leader. People loved working for these women. They were experts and pioneered their way through technical issues. They didn't just have a full client load; they led the women's emerging leadership group in their firm, or they led a group of employees in giving back their time at local nonprofits. Clients loved working with these women. And the partners of the firms loved how much work these women did for them.

My time away from the profession gave me fresh eyes to see what I had never noticed before. Of the eight women on stage, all were white or had light skin. Because each of them talked about being married with children, I suspected they were likely heterosexual. I didn't see any physical aids like walking canes, seeing eye dogs, or wheelchairs, so I assumed they were able-bodied. And I noticed the size of their bodies. The majority of them were very thin, likely a size six or lower.

That evening I asked my husband and kids why there weren't outstanding leadership luncheons for men. But I knew the answer the moment the question left my lips. They didn't need one. Men didn't need to be retained. Men were already known leaders and they were already successful in public accounting. Celebrating them would be fruitless and unnecessary.

Thinking back to my earlier career in public accounting, I knew of many male partners who didn't have the same resume these women had. I worked for plenty of them who weren't great to work with. Plenty of them were average technically. Plenty of them weren't leading the way to give back to our communities or build our corporate culture.

The revelation made me sick, but it wasn't surprising. The accounting profession wanted to attract more women, but not any kind of woman leader. They wanted one who did it all. The CPA profession was asking us to drink their Kool-Aid: a medley of excellence, hard work, likability, service, dedication. But equally important, the standard of outstanding leadership for women wasn't just perfect work performance, it also included a perfect body.

What I thought would be a fairly innocuous event turned out to be a slap in the face. Were these eight women successful because they were thin and "perfect"? Or did they need to be thin and perfect to be successful?

Was their thinness and perfection just a coincidence? Was it causation? Or correlation?

AVERAGE ISN'T ENOUGH

When I began my accounting career over twenty-five years before the conference, I chose to join the only public accounting firm with a woman partner. Back in 1992, when there wasn't one female CEO on the Inc. 500 list, it wasn't surprising that out of six firms, only one had a female partner in Boston.[1] I assumed the powers that be at my firm recognized and appreciated women. If they acknowledged our partner as equal and promoted her through the ranks, they could do the same for me.

Susan was legendary and often the subject of discussion during team lunch breaks. We heard stories about how she would be on her car cell phone, talking to her secretary and taking client calls. Back in the early 1990s, now-commonplace occurrences like that were unheard of. But we understood that Susan was doing it all. She was a partner in a prestigious firm. She was front and center when recruiting and hiring young talent. She was attractive. She was slim and always dressed impeccably. She had a young child at home.

As I considered how I too could have it all—family, professional success, happiness—thankfully I had Susan. She was blazing the trail. I thought if she could do it, maybe I could do it too. I just needed to do what she did.

I can't speak to the obstacles Susan had to overcome to achieve one of the highest ranks in my firm. I'm assuming there were many, or there wouldn't have been just one Susan—there would have been Susan, Julie, Nancy, and Mary. But what I can speak to is what I witnessed. Susan was a Wellesley College graduate. She was white. She was thin. She didn't stand out because she was the only woman; she stood out because she was performing at the highest level, with her clients and for the firm.

In the documentary *RBG*, the Honorable Ruth Bader Ginsburg shared her experience finding her first job in the late 1970s when she graduated from Columbia Law School after transferring from Harvard, where she was one of the very few students who made the *Harvard Law Review*. Not a single firm would hire her. At the time, being one of the brightest legal minds in the country wasn't enough for a woman to get hired by a New York City law firm.

Time passed and thankfully opportunities changed slowly as the Honorable Bader Ginsburg progressed in her career, eventually rising to the highest court in the country. On her way there, she performed at the highest possible level for her profession. There are stories of her working through the night after caring for her child, night after night after night. Her tenacity and drive knew no bounds.

I don't know of a single *average* woman who makes their way to the upper echelons of their profession. Do you? I can think of a few men who do. I'm sure you can, too. Susan and Ruth were goddesses. While they were making history, they were inspiring and educating everyone around them about what's required for women to rise.

Access to power doesn't get granted to just any woman. They have to be exceptional. They have to be superhuman. They have to be perfect.

PERFECTION LIES IN THE EYES OF THE BEHOLDER

Expectations of perfection aren't just prevalent in the workplace. They extend to our home lives and communities, too: running our households, caring for our loved ones, volunteering at our kids' schools, and participating in our churches or synagogues.

In today's world, we pretty much know who the perfect woman is. She's smart, but not so smart that she's overconfident. She's lovely and may even be sweet, but she's not timid and someone you can step all over. She spends time on her appearance, but she's not vain. She's a great mom, and even if she works outside the house, she puts her kids first no matter what. She's a good wife and keeps a clean and lovely HGTV-worthy home, but she isn't too meticulous. She's not afraid to complain to you about the endless amount of laundry to do, but she gets the laundry done.

The standard for what a perfect woman looks like changes depending on the woman's circumstances. If you're religious, your version of the perfect woman may pray regularly and go to church. If you're athletic, your version of the perfect woman may forgo church and catch up with her running group or go to her favorite yoga class on Sunday mornings. And if you're ambitious, love your career, and run your own business, your version of the perfect woman does it all, on top of prioritizing her passions and desire to make a huge difference in the world.

Perfection has a way of seeping into the smallest details of our lives. Natalie, a client who worked with me on her relationship with food, felt so guilty when the dinners she put on her family's kitchen table weren't healthy enough because they were from a box, frozen package, or take-out container. Natalie believed a good mom fed her family well, which meant making meals she never had time to shop for—much less prepare—because of her demanding job.

What you consider perfect is likely what you've been told or shown, implicitly or explicitly. Earlier in my career, I assessed my perfection based on others' opinions.

When I was working a part-time schedule with full-time responsibilities as a finance director for a growing consulting firm while my kids were toddlers, I was trying to be perfect for each of my constituents. I needed to meet every deadline and make my boss happy. I needed to pick up the kids from daycare on time so my daycare provider and my kids were happy. I needed to serve a vegetable with every dinner.

Perfection may not manifest in obvious ways; it can also disguise itself. You may think you are doing things right or being good when really, you're only trying to achieve perfection. When I was in kindergarten, my mother sent me off to school with a casual reminder: "Be a good girl and listen to everything the teacher says." I got the message. To be good, I needed to do what I was told. That's how I could be perfect.

IT'S A MATTER OF CURRENCY

Because women haven't had equal rights and opportunities, we need currency as a way of gaining economic, social, and political power. Like money, currency is something we can exchange for something we want. Back in my day, sought-after Devil Dogs had lots of currency in the school lunchroom. When my kids empty the dishwasher and clean out the kitty litter with few complaints, they earn lots of currency when they want something. We have more power and influence when we have currency.

It may seem implausible right now, but it's only been a short while since women in the United States have had the ability to earn a living without the help of a male figure in their life. It wasn't until the passage of the Married Women's Property Act in 1848 and the Act Concerning the Rights and Liabilities of Husband and Wife in 1860, which all states adopted by 1900, that allowed married women to own property.[2] It wasn't until the Equal Opportunity Credit Act of 1974 that women were allowed to have their own bank account or loan without a signature from their husband or male relative.[3]

Yes, laws have changed and women have more access to jobs, capital, and financial security than they ever have. But you can't argue with the pay gap, the rate in which women are paid less for the same work men do. The most recent report from the American Association of University Women (AAUW) shared that white women are paid $0.79 for every dollar of similar work that a white man earns. Asian women fare the best and are paid $0.87. Black women earn $0.63, American Indian women earn $0.60, and Hispanic women earn $0.55.[4]

Sure, progress has been made in female representation in politics, academia, and corporate America, yet there is no debating these numbers. Women aren't afforded equal opportunity and equal pay. Aside from Asian women, women of color are faring far worse than white women.

Say you gathered a group of poker players: a white man, an Asian woman, a white woman, and a Hispanic woman. If you applied the pay gap to the game, each player wouldn't be equal. For the $1,000 the white man has to start the game, the Asian woman has $870, the white woman has $790, and the Hispanic woman brings $550. No matter what kind of hand they were dealt, it's obvious who has the highest chance of winning. Besides the white man, what can the rest of the players do to try to win?

They must find other forms of currency.

JODY'S VISION BOARD

In high school, my friend Jody pinned a magazine ad on her wall that said, "You can never be too thin, too rich or too beautiful" with a picture of a stunning model. Jody was a pioneer in creating vision boards before most of us knew how impactful pictures and words could be on our unconscious minds in helping to create our dreams.

When I first read those words, I was laying on Jody's bed. She and I were sharing a bag of Cool Ranch Doritos and drinking Diet Coke. I wasn't so much struck by the assumptions behind the words as I was by Jody's willingness to put her desires on her wall for others to see.

I knew well before that moment that my body wasn't thin or beautiful. I knew I was supposed to have a smaller body. I heard it growing up whenever my mother was dieting and wondering aloud what was wrong with her body. I heard it when I was called a "brute" on the middle school playground because I looked different from my cute, pretty, ponytail-wearing friends. I saw it when I watched episodes of *The Dukes of Hazzard* and *Solid Gold Dancers* and movies like *Grease* and *Dirty Dancing*. I saw it when I looked at the pictures in *Teen* and *People* magazine.

My body was tall and strong, not thin. Pretty girls had thin bodies. Seeing Jody's pinup shook me. As I was munching on Doritos, I was also thinking to myself, *How can Jody eat these and stay so thin?* I had already been dieting for a few years and was trying to be thinner. Until that point, I thought the desire for thinness was only reserved for girls like me, the ones with broad shoulders and big bones. I didn't realize that thin girls needed a reminder to stay thin.

If Jody and I did have one thing in common besides our love of Doritos, it was our social class. Our small town in Massachusetts was primarily white and middle class. Even though our families had financial security, and there was always enough food to put on the table, money wasn't as abundant as it was with some of our friends. We didn't ski like Sara and her family did. We didn't have our own cars. One day at school my friends were whispering about what Tracy's dad bought for her birthday: three cashmere sweaters. I didn't even know what cashmere was.

The ad on Jody's wall was the epitome of our social conditioning. But my sixteen-year-old mind hadn't been educated, nor did it understand culture, sexism, and marketing strategy. I read Jody's poster on the wall like marching orders. For the first time, the words were right in front of my eyes. *Got it*, I thought. If I wanted to be happy, desirable, and successful, I needed to be rich, thin, and beautiful. I needed to be perfect.

COMMENTS IN OFFICE
HALLWAYS AND ELEVATORS

Sixty-plus hours was the norm when I was working in public accounting in my early twenties. My weight had been fluctuating five to fifteen pounds since middle school, and I'd often exercise intensely and go on fad diets to maintain my weight. After a few months of working very long hours on a few clients with no time to work out, I started a low-fat diet and workout program at my gym with help from a trainer. After a few months of following the recipes to a T and finding time to exercise again, I lost some weight. And people noticed. Including Helen.

For such a tiny woman, Helen was that one person in the office who had a mighty presence. She could make everyone's lives a living nightmare because she managed the staffing schedule. She could staff you on the best client or the worst. I had always tried to be friendly to Helen, but she never returned the warmth.

One late evening in the office, Helen joined me on the elevator. I immediately noticed how she looked me up and down. My stomach clenched and I wished for somewhere to hide from her gaze. A gaze she wasn't trying to hide from me. "You look great, Tara. You've lost weight," she said. Finally, I was getting attention from her. Just not the kind I wanted. I felt so exposed. I didn't want Helen to notice my weight loss because if she did, she would surely notice my weight gain. My body weight was under a microscope for Helen to decide whether I was successful or a failure. A determination made without her looking at a single performance review. And I knew the next busy client was right around the corner, when I wouldn't be able to get to the gym as often as I needed to.

A few years later, after I left public accounting and was working in the financial planning department for a large hospital, I bumped into Steve, one of the accounting partners I had worked with. I was a month from getting married and was once again putting a lot of time and energy into keeping my weight down. After a few moments of seeing me, Steve said, "Wow, Tara, you look great." Unlike Helen, Steve didn't explicitly mention my body weight. But he didn't have to.

My body size fluctuations didn't go unnoticed, especially by those who essentially signed my paycheck. They were seeing me in my smaller body, and they weren't shy about affirming me because of it. Women's bodies are on a runway with no black curtain. Our bodies are noticed, whether worthy of praise or deemed invisible. There is no escaping the 24/7 viewing and the chance that anyone may notice and comment on our body size. It's happening in our corporate office hallways and elevators.

THE CEO STUDY

It turns out that my observations from the women's leadership luncheon were pretty accurate.

In 2009, researchers wanted to understand if weight bias could be impacting the glass ceiling that women experience in the workplace.[5] The glass ceiling refers to the invisible barriers that impact the advancement of women, minorities, and marginalized identities in the workplace. Weight bias includes assumptions, judgments, stereotypes, and discriminatory acts toward people because of their body weight.

This study's authors asked, "Do female and male CEOs have the same body size as the average population?" They examined male CEOs of Fortune 100 companies and female CEOs of Fortune 1000 companies. This was a bit tricky because they didn't have access to each CEO's body weight, so the researchers had experts in evaluating body weight rate the CEOs' bodies based on pictures. There is certainly subjectivity to this research, but the conclusion is compelling: an estimated 5-22 percent of women CEOs and 45-61 percent of men CEOs were overweight. Compare that to the population of adults over twenty; 28 percent of women and 34 percent of men being overweight in 2007–2008, as determined by a body mass index over 25.[6] It's clear that at the time, female CEOs were disproportionately slimmer than the average American woman and that male CEOs were disproportionately larger than the average American man.

The data are eye-opening. Men who were CEOs of a Fortune 100 company were more likely to have a larger body as almost 50 percent of those men are overweight. For women CEOs, the preference is thinness.

When I found this study, I felt oddly comforted knowing other folks are noticing the prevalence of thinness among women in corporate America. For women, having a large body is a barrier to entry among the higher ranks. Whether size is cause or correlation, successful women in corporate America must be thinner than the average woman. The opposite is true of men. This study confirms what we've been seeing with our own eyes on the cover of *Forbes*, on the steps of the Capitol, in commencement addresses given by our highest educators, and from well-established influencers in our social media feeds.

THE PROMISE OF THE THIN AND PERFECT

I had sat through plenty of business luncheons and networking events before that women's leadership luncheon in 2019. I had been in awe of women who had climbed the ranks and sat in board meetings among men. But I never thought twice about their bodies until I had fresh eyes.

Now it's all I see. It's been in front of you and me this whole time. This is more than just a desire to be thin or to be the woman who does it all. Much more. This has been a requirement. Helen shared this obligation with me on our way out of the office that late evening. Steve reminded me of it when I bumped into him in the hallway. And the writing was on Jody's wall, literally and figuratively. The CEO body size study just confirmed

what we already knew. If thinness wasn't a requirement of success for women, then we'd see female CEOs
wearing dress sizes above a six or an eight. After all, the
average woman's dress size is 16.[7] This requirement is
really an unspoken contract, one that we've unknowingly entered into.

Thinness and perfection aren't requirements only
reserved for corporate America. We see the same standards upheld in Hollywood, on runways, in the White
House, at PTO meetings at our kids' schools. These
standards apply to every woman and person identifying
as female. If the standards did not exist, we would see
a wider variety of women's bodies on our social media
feeds, and there wouldn't be a self-care movement for
women who forgo caring for themselves while striving
for perfection.

I call this the Promise of the Thin and Perfect. With
any promise, there is an expectation of something in
return. We've been told we need to have a thin body,
that we need to be perfect by meeting the ideals which
have been established for us and that when we do, we'll
be successful. Thin and Perfect is the requirement for
women's success.

This is why my clients tell me they'd feel more successful in life if they lost weight. Each accomplishment
that came from trying to be perfect had a necessary

companion: a thin body. Without a thin body, any accomplishment didn't feel complete. It was missing something. They would get promoted or earn a bonus big enough to take the family to Europe for two weeks. They'd land a huge client or do an amazing job on a massive project. But if they weren't happy with their body because they had extra weight, celebrating felt unnecessary. Without a thin body, their accomplishments fell short.

And vice versa—women who live in a thin body have told me they feel an emptiness with their accomplishments. Those rare moments are followed by *What's next?* They can never rest and never relax. They aren't allowed to celebrate or acknowledge their outstanding skills and hard work because the path to perfection doesn't have a finish line. Thinness is something they must protect and maintain, and they often feel lost and wayward, chasing something that doesn't leave them fulfilled or truly happy.

The Promise of the Thin and Perfect has been living and breathing inside you. The clear cultural messages we've received around thinness and perfection have created a belief system within us. We all have thousands of beliefs, the majority of which come from cultural narratives. But the Promise of the Thin and Perfect is much more than a set of beliefs. It's a complex mechanism that triggers a very predictable and complex set of reactions and behaviors. Those reactions and behaviors are as destructive and dangerous as the belief system itself.

This is why we need to name this mechanism. It needs to be called out. It takes on a life of its own, and when it's living inside us, we are being compromised. The Promise of the Thin and Perfect is one of the most critical issues facing women's sovereignty. Its promise is success, but from what I've observed, it only leaves women feeling trapped, hopeless, and defeated. It's also putting women's health at risk. There is a good chance that as the ambitious, bright, and motivated woman you are, you want to make a massive difference in the world. But you're exhausted and wondering what you're doing wrong because you're working your ass off trying to do everything right.

The Promise of the Thin and Perfect changes how we engage with ourselves, our bodies, and the world. It's created a way for us to think about *who* we need to be in our lives to feel successful, attractive and worthy. Now that you know what the Promise of the Thin and Perfect is, let's explore how you've been fulfilling it. Let's discover what's happening in our minds and hearts. Going forward, I'll be referring to the Promise of the Thin and Perfect as simply, the Promise.

CHAPTER 2

STRATEGIES

When you stumble upon a problem, you naturally want strategies to solve it. You have a leaky faucet, you call a plumber. You want to start sleeping better at night, you create a new nighttime routine. Strategies move us forward. We use them to get shit done. Not only have we been engaging in the Promise of the Thin and Perfect, we've been offered strategies and tactics to fulfill it. And in some cases, we've been offered the strategies before we even knew we had a problem that needed fixing.

DIETING AS A WAY OF LIFE

We've all heard the ubiquitous statement "If you want to lose weight, go on a diet." This is gospel. We've read versions of this in news articles. Heard it from daytime talk show hosts like Ellen and Oprah. And maybe even heard it from people close to us, like our gym teachers, coaches, friends, aunts, and mothers. It's readily understood that if people want to lose weight, they need to restrict how many calories they eat every day, omit certain food groups from their diet, and exercise to burn calories.

Forty-five million Americans are dieting every year. Weight loss is now a $72 billion industry that offers people plenty of ways to lose weight.[8] Massive weight loss companies like Weight Watchers (WW)[9] and Jenny Craig[10] trade shares on the stock exchange. Companies offer weight loss supplements like shakes, teas, and other drinks. The pharmaceutical industry offers weight loss drugs to reduce people's appetites, speed up their metabolism, and keep them from binging. Dieting is so pervasive, you may not know too many people who aren't trying to lose weight. You may even be comfortable with the extremes people take to lose weight.

JANE FONDA, SUGAR-FREE BUBBLE GUM, AND JUICE CLEANSES

Dieting wasn't a choice I consciously made when I was twelve; I just did what everyone around me was doing. Growing up in the '70s, I watched Jane Fonda in her leotard doing donkey kicks and Richard Simmons in his headband, dancing and offering words of encouragement. When I would sleep over at my grand-mother's house, I would eat a bowl of ice cream (she always had vanilla ice cream in the freezer), then sneak into the kitchen while Grammy was watching Lawrence Welk and do a set of twenty or so donkey kicks. My mom always had Tab and Sweet'N Low in the house and kept a small white food scale to the left of the kitchen sink. She tracked and logged everything she ate in her spiral-bound, white, lined notebook. While my brother and I ate spaghetti and meatballs watching *Happy Days* in our living room, my mother ate roasted chicken and salad. It was clear to me that dieting was something to work at, and losing weight meant you did things that not everyone else did.

My weight loss strategies continued for decades while my weight cycled up and down by ten or so pounds. When my weight crept up, I would just look for the next diet. When I wasn't on a formal diet, I was still trying to eat the right foods in the right amounts. Each diet was programmed with a set of rules: what a portion size was, what foods to avoid to prevent weight gain, what foods to eat more of because they were healthy.

Throughout the years, weight loss schemes have changed. In high school and college, I was eating low-fat bread and low-fat ice cream. While studying in college, I would try to keep myself from eating by drinking Diet

Coke and chewing gum. I chewed pack after pack of Carefree Sugarless Bubble Gum until my jaw hurt.

Aside from dieting, exercise was my go-to strategy to manage my weight, and there was no limit to how many miles I'd run or how much time I'd spend in the gym. I would run up to fourteen miles every Thanksgiving morning so I could eat stuffing, mashed potatoes, and pumpkin pie somewhat guilt-free.

In the early 2000s, I started practicing yoga in communities filled with yogis practicing the ayurveda diet, macrobiotics diet, raw food diet, and juice and smoothie cleanses. Around the same time, weight loss programs started to change. Instead of diets, there were ways to "change your lifestyle," "eat clean," and "get healthy." I now had an even better reason to control what I ate. I was putting better food in my body so I could be a better yogi.

Once again, I ran in circles with people who were doing what I was trying to do: earn a slimmer and therefore better body. I owned a juicer and blender, which I sometimes took with me when I traveled so I could be healthy on the road. I once did an eleven-day juice cleanse with a close friend, and we shared recipes and rooted each other on. One friend offered me this advice while I was cleansing: when you're too hungry at night, just go to bed and sleep away the discomfort.

Since dieting and eating healthy was a way of life, food and the number on the scale were always on my mind. Because my weight fluctuated regularly, I was always beating myself up for not controlling myself around food and sticking to my healthy meal plans. I understood the sacrifices I needed to make. Unfortunately, all these strategies didn't lead to permanent weight loss. It only made me obsess about food and feel like a failure.

ARE YOU DIETING?

Megan, a client, put it perfectly: "I thought dieting was just what every woman did." Living in the 1930s, Megan might have concluded the same thing about smoking, considering that in the first half of the twentieth century, more than half of adults living in an industrialized nation smoked cigarettes.[11] But prevalence doesn't mean smoking or dieting aren't harmful. Like Megan, dieting may just be a part of your life. After all, you're trying to fulfill the Promise of the Thin and Perfect so you can feel happy and be successful.

Diets are now even more in disguise, just like those my fellow yogis and I followed. They are called "protocols," "lifestyle plans," "metabolism resets," and other such names that feel empowering, that make you feel you have invested in your wellness. Dieters now look down on formal diets that are just about weight loss;

instead, they embrace diets focused on wellness. These diets are all essentially the same, they've just been marketed differently.

At the time of this writing, I counted 97 Facebook Groups that included the term "sugar detox" and 89 Facebook Groups that included "sugar free." None of the groups mentions the word "diet," even though the mission of its members is to abstain from a certain food—which is the definition of the word diet. Instead, they market with taglines like "live peacefully without sugar" and "break up with sugar for good." Food tracking apps are the norm for folks who want to gain control over what they eat and how many calories they burn. Eighty-seven million people used a fitness or health tracker app every month in 2020, which is roughly 30 percent of adults with smartphones.[12] The majority of these folks are between eighteen and twenty-nine years old. MyFitnessPal, one of the more popular apps, doesn't mention weight loss on their homepage.[13] They say, "Good health starts with what you eat. Want to eat more mindfully? Track meals, learn about your habits, and reach your goals with MyFitnessPal." Along with our health, mindfulness is another incentive diet companies are using to motivate people to diet.

If you're dieting, your experiences with weight loss are likely similar to mine. You've sacrificed with an empty and uncomfortable belly, and the weight just keeps coming back. In addition to experiencing this vicious cycle, you know you're dieting if you're:

- Labeling certain foods as good and certain ones as bad.
- Eliminating or reducing types of food, like sugar, starches, fruits, or dairy.
- Weighing yourself regularly.
- Eating based on portion sizes and not hunger or fullness.
- Using workouts as a way to burn calories.
- Engaging in cleanses, clean eating, intermittent fasting, or simply trying to "eat better" as a way to reset yourself.

The best way to really know if you're dieting is how guilty or ashamed you feel if you just ate something you considered wrong or bad. Following a diet is following a set of rules someone else gave you. When you feel guilty about breaking those rules, you know you're following a diet.

HARDWORKING, EDUCATED, AND NICE WOMEN

Food rules aren't the only rules we follow unknowingly. To get ahead and claim equal opportunity in the workplace with men, women have had to work both outside and inside the house. I don't need to tell you that according to social norms, women are responsible for caring for the kids and their home. So, when we work outside the home, our workload doesn't stay the same. The kids need to be driven around, dinner needs to be put on the table, laundry has to be washed and folded, and countertops need to be wiped down. In my house, my husband helps with a ton of these tasks, but this seems to be the exception. In a 2019 Gallup poll examining household responsibilities, women are still largely holding the traditional roles of laundry, cleaning, caring for the children, grocery shopping, doing the dishes, and paying the bills. Men are still primarily handling car and lawn maintenance and investment decisions.[14]

Another rule we adhere to is getting educated. A great education is a woman's best way to create opportunities for themselves and increase their chances at career advancement. Women hold more undergraduate and graduate degrees than men at 57 percent and 59 percent, respectively.[15] It was shocking to speak with some female students about this discrepancy at my alma mater after I had given a talk at a women's leadership conference there. Many shared with me their double majors and their various extracurricular activities, which they often led. One major wasn't enough. One club or program wasn't enough. These nineteen- and twenty-year-old women had gotten themselves out of bed early on a Saturday morning, put on their business suits, and spent the day at a leadership conference. I wondered what their male classmates were doing that day. When I Googled men's leadership conferences at my university the only one I could find was for Black men.[16] It's not that men weren't at a leadership conference; it's that women needed to be.

Being ultra productive is another rule we follow in our pursuit of perfection. At one talk I gave to college students, Emily shared an unspoken game she and her roommates often played. They would each complain about how stressed out they were, trying to show each other who was the busiest and had the most demanding class load. The most exhausted and overwhelmed roommate unspokenly won. Until the next day, when they played the game again and a new winner would be crowned. This trend of busyness and the accompanying stress is supported by research. When examining work ethic between men and women, one study determined that women are 10 percent more productive than men.[17] From my own experience with clients, not only are they more productive; they're more stressed and overwhelmed, too.

While we are going above and beyond, it's important that we're nice and considerate of other people's needs, too. In middle school, I watched an afterschool special on how to make friends. I was so excited about this information because, like many of us at that age, I felt awkward and insecure about making friends. Now I had the secrets that would make all my problems go away, that would help me fit in and be liked.

The next day, I put my new friendly-persons' lessons to the test during my English class. When we were asked to come to the front of the class to pick up our homework for the evening, I also picked up Kelly's homework for her. Kelly sat in front of me. This was something I never thought to do before. Kelly smiled, somewhat surprised at my new act of kindness, and thanked me.

Our training to be nice girls starts early in life. Nice girls smile. Nice girls go out of their way for other people. Nice girls think of other people's feelings and needs, often above their own. Not that I was a mean girl before, but being nice became a requirement for me, almost an addiction. I needed those around me to like me.

Is it wrong to be a kind person? Is it wrong to work hard? Is it wrong to be healthy? Of course not. Just like it's not wrong to be educated or more efficient. We've been conditioned to strive for perfection as a strategy to fulfill the Promise without knowing there was a problem to solve. But striving for perfection is how we show the world an ideal version of ourselves, often dismissing our own values, needs, and desires.

How often do you put others' needs ahead of your own? How often do you forgo sleep and sanity to meet a deadline and perform a project to your own standards? Just like "dieting" is a code word for being healthy, pursuing perfection is disguised as working hard and being nice, humble, and extremely competent. And just like dieting, being perfect is reaching an ideal we didn't define for ourselves, but one that has been defined for us.

The demands on women's time and energy have only increased as a sacrifice they need to make to get ahead in their careers. We've proven and continue to prove how bright we are, how productive we are, how good we are at juggling work and home life, and how kind we can be. We've been diligently following the rules set for us, fulfilling the Promise. Yet despite all our efforts, women hold only 23 percent of executive positions and 29 percent of the senior leadership positions in corporate America.[18]

THREE BUSINESSES AND THREE KIDS

I was determined to do it all. So much so that for a few years, I was simultaneously running three different businesses on top of all my other responsibilities. One was a lucrative accounting consulting firm that leveraged my expertise and long-standing career experience as a CPA.

Another was a yoga studio that created community and connection and touched so many lives. Another was my coaching practice around body image and relationships with food, which was the container for healing my past struggles and my vision for a better future for countless women. I never imagined I'd be doing all this, but I made one business decision after another, each making perfect sense at the time.

Even with three young children at home, I wanted to be a working mom who contributed financially, share a yoga practice I loved, and make a meaningful impact on the world. But what didn't make sense was the amount of work and the weight of the pressure I felt. I could never find enough time no matter how early I woke up or how late I went to bed. I'd often multitask by taking calls while driving the kids to their sports practices or checking email while watching TV with the family. I felt a constant panic that I would drop the ball and let someone down. Forgoing sleep was my way of trying to keep this anxiety at bay.

If I was busy with a work deadline, I'd panic when the school called because my kid was sick and needed a pickup. I'd think, *Can't they spend the rest of the day in the nurse's office so I can just get this one last thing done? Am I a horrible mom for even wanting that?* I had so many competing priorities, it was impossible to meet them all. Meanwhile, I continued to exercise regularly, not willing to forgo long runs or ninety-minute hot, sweaty yoga classes. I had to be the good girl. The hard working entrepreneur. The working mom who didn't miss a baseball game or a football practice pickup. And—the irony wasn't lost on me—I needed to be the peaceful and mindful yogi who ran a yoga studio.

I was a shape-shifter, inside and out. I'd straighten my unruly curly hair on the days I was working at a client's office and wear my Lululemon yoga pants and mala beads on the days I taught yoga. I'd often coach clients into the evening, when the kids were already settled in their beds. I was holding on so tightly to the ideas I had with every professional role that I could barely hold together mothering, being a wife, and running a household. I wasn't telling myself that I needed to be perfect because I never felt like I was even close to perfect. I was saying, I can't let anyone down. I can't make anyone upset. I have to keep going and be the best I can be. I don't want to fail. I don't want anyone to be disappointed in me. These were my code words to describe striving for perfection.

I didn't know who I was; I only knew what was expected of me. When someone would ask me what I did for a living, I would often answer with the version of me I wanted them to see. I wasn't just an accountant. And god forbid, I wasn't just a yogi. And I wasn't just a coach. I was among the elite because I could do all three businesses and still be a mother and wife. I was so willing to be overextended and overworked so I could feel my version of perfect. I didn't realize it at the time, but when they responded with, "Wow—that's incredible. How do you do it all?" I felt like I had just risen a few notches in esteem.

When we show the world how productive, organized, and busy we are, we believe we are preventing external criticism. I can now see how freakin' crazy I was, but I had justified it all. Being so busy became a habit that allowed me to earn external validation. All I knew was the hustle. There was no sanity in this. With three young kids at home, I showed them a mother who was often frantic and overwhelmed. Today, my family and I can joke about how often I was late picking them up from sports practices, and the time I was at my youngest son's baseball game and missed his big hit because I was answering an email. I didn't have the bandwidth to give everything my full attention.

One winter school break, we rented a home near a ski mountain in Vermont with close family friends. Part of me was excited for time away to hang out, be with the kids, and get away from work. Another part of me felt like I didn't have the luxury to take time off from my businesses.

When I was catching up with our friends the night we arrived, I shared what my life was like with Lori, an attorney and also a busy working mom. I told her I needed to just put my head down and work my way out of the overwhelm. That was the only solution I could entertain. I was determined. I knew this was a lot, but I didn't see any other way. I couldn't let go, and I couldn't say no.

The next day was one of those rare, but gorgeous New England ski days. It was snowing that morning, and this meant fresh powder! On our first run after lunch, I was trying to avoid a rider in front of me and fell backward. To stop myself from sliding, I reached back to brace myself. Immediately, I felt a surge of pain through my shoulder. I had torn my rotator cuff and had surgery a week or so later. My busy schedule came to a grinding halt.

With three businesses and three kids, I couldn't take it any longer. I was emotionally and energetically holding the weight of the world. It was too much. My body knew it, even if my mind didn't. I wouldn't halt my busyness and drive for perfection, so a benevolent power had to step in and make me slow down.

I thought my busy schedule and my accomplishments would make me feel happier and more successful. After all, I needed to earn it! But this feeling I was so desperate for was always out of reach. While I was busy working tirelessly, I was just putting my happiness on hold. And I was hiding my true self, showing the world a version of me I thought they wanted to see.

ARE YOU PURSUING PERFECTION?

You may be wondering, *When haven't I been striving for perfection?* Ha! Great question. Just like me, striving and excelling is your MO. At the heart of pursuing perfection is the drive to fix yourself and show the world a better version of yourself. There is a difference between pursuing perfection for people to think more favorably of you and needing to perform so you feel like you're a better person. Remember, the Promise has been assumed; you've been using strategies to fulfill this contract without your conscious consent.

Now that this unspoken contract has a name, we can call it out and speak about it. And we can discern our own actions as a reaction to the Promise.

I've shared with you the common ways we prove ourselves that are centered around receiving external validation. That could be a smile, a hug, a client's testimonial, a positive book review, a raise, a new project, an invite to a neighbor's party. We may even feel validated and successful when our children perform well. All of this is outside of our control.

When pursuing perfection, we are often attached to the results of each action we take. When I was studying endlessly, I was doing it to earn an A. Not to get a better handle on the subject matter of the class. If that had been the case, I probably would have been happy with half the studying as that's what it would have taken for me to know enough. Ask yourself, *If no one notices, would I do what I'm doing the same way?*

I invite you to question all the choices you make. Do they align with what's important to you, or do they feel like an obligation? Another way to look at it is: What cost do you pay to pursue perfection? Do you forgo sleep and downtime? Do you find yourself exhausted after being around a group of people because you feel like you have to be extra nice or extra funny or extra entertaining?

There are even sneakier ways you may be pursuing perfection that have the impact of waiting and hiding. Waiting is when we don't move forward toward something desirable until we feel like we are enough. Sadly, because the Promise never allows us to be enough, we may be waiting for a very long time. Possibly forever.

Waiting has that conditional element to it: when I have x, I will y. When I've lost ten pounds, I'll go on my dream vacation. When I have enough education, I'll apply for my dream job. When I have enough money in my bank account, I'll start my own business.

Waiting may seem practical. But often, it is just a way for us to negotiate out of what we really want. Because the Promise tells us we need to fulfill thinness and perfection first. And then we get what we want. We can't have our dreams until we've fulfilled our end of the deal and reached a standard of perfection that someone else defined for us. This is a vicious cycle that only keeps us feeling empty and stuck.

Hiding is the conditioning we've received to not be seen, heard, or felt. We physically hide our bodies, silence our voices, and withhold our feelings. Obvious ways of hiding include wearing dark and oversized clothing to not draw attention to yourself. When you speak to a large group, you may speak behind a podium so no one can see your whole body. You may join Zoom calls with the camera off. You also may hide when you prefer to say the nice and "right" thing instead of what you really think. The not-so-obvious ways of hiding include not sharing your thoughts and opinions. When someone asks how you're feeling, your response is, "I'm fine." You couldn't possibly share your anger, sadness, or frustration.

Being inauthentic is being fake or superficial, and authenticity is sharing our true selves and being real. No one wants to be inauthentic. If you're not sure who that real woman is living inside you, that's because of the Promise. The strategies of dieting, proving, waiting, and hiding are so normal, you don't realize they've been masking your true self.

The Promise is built on the foundation that women aren't enough. By blindly engaging in the Promise's strategies, we've bought into the belief that there is something about us and our bodies that needs fixing. And if you can't fix yourself, if you can't be both thin and perfect, then you better not show yourself at all. You better keep trying to prove yourself and wait for good things to come. Writing this takes the air out of my lungs.

The Promise has been requiring us to be both thin *and* perfect. Bring some gentle awareness to this deception. Now ask yourself an important (and often annoying!) question:

How's striving to be thin and perfect working out for you?

CHAPTER 3

DIETING

If there wasn't anything wrong with your body, would you have needed to go on your first diet? Put another way, if your body was perfect as is, would you need to adjust the way you eat and exercise to change its size and shape?

Of course not.

Some people spend their whole lives trying to be thin by dieting. After they've gone off one diet and have gained the weight back that they initially lost, they look for another one. As Erica, a friend and member of my community, said, "Weight loss is always the be-all and end-all." Yet, despite how desperate people are to slim down by dieting, 95 percent of diets lead to long-term weight gain.[19] I wish I had known the truth about dieting, like I do now. If I had, I might have thought twice when I gave my money to Weight Watchers. Not just once, but twice. This information has been readily available for decades. If someone had told me diets weren't effective then I didn't hear it. Weight loss coaches and organizations didn't hear it either—or didn't want to.

Let's pull the curtain back on dieting and understand why it has been so accepted and normalized, despite how ineffective diets are. And let's get clear about the real impact of dieting.

GLORY AND WORRY

I know you've lost weight successfully. At least once. You can probably recall the moment when you reached your goal weight, just like you remember your graduation or wedding day. You had to buy new, smaller-sized clothing. It was glorious. You felt like a rock star, and everyone told you how fantastic you looked.

After being on Weight Watchers for a few months, my husband took me on a shopping spree for my thirty-first birthday. I thought I had this whole weight loss thing figured out. Track my points, make huge batches of veggie soup, pack big-ass salads for lunch, and go for long runs when I overate. As I tried on outfit after outfit in the dressing room, I was in awe of the sizes that fit me and the reflection of my hips and belly in the full-length mirror. *Whose body is this?* I thought. We walked out of that store filled with excitement. My husband was happy that I was happy. I was happy for myself, for my body, and for how loved I felt.

While a part of me felt on top of the world, another part of me doubted I could stay there. With so many of my family members and friends noticing my slimmer body, I felt exposed. Now that people around me knew what I was capable of, I felt pressure to keep dieting. I wasn't just trying to follow the meal plan, I *had* to follow the meal plan. What's more embarrassing and more shameful than needing to lose weight? Losing weight and gaining it back. I didn't relax when I hit my weight loss goal because I knew it was just the beginning. Instead of basking in my weight loss glory, I worried that weight gain would make me a bigger failure.

You may have felt like a rock star when the scale went down. Wasn't it a fleeting moment of glory accompanied by lots of dread and worry?

Two years after my initial weight loss on Weight Watchers, after I had my second child, my weight crept right back up where it was the first time. I tried Weight Watchers again. After all, I thought I knew the formula. It was just a matter of executing the plan. My weight loss success memory was fueling me, inspiring me to lose weight again. It was a common-sense approach—if you can do something once, you should be able to do it again.

But I couldn't. I'd conveniently forget to log in my points each day. I'd make the veggie soup, and it would sit in my fridge all week untouched. The smell of it even turned my stomach. Each morning, I'd promise myself that I'd be good that day and follow the plan. Then, when I was hungry around 10:00 a.m., I'd have a bagel with cream cheese from the dozen bagels that Lori from HR left in the office kitchen. They were so fresh and soft, I couldn't pass them up. After the bagel, it was all over. I couldn't possibly log those bagel points into the app. So the whole day was gone. The bagel was the start. After that I'd snack on M&M's on our office manager Kathy's desk and would eat a few slices of pizza during our team lunch.

I didn't take my diet failure lightly, and I'm sure you haven't either. I naturally wished away my overwhelming guilt. I wished I could hide for fear that someone would know I ate too much. I tried to ease my guilt by promising myself I'd do better next time. But I couldn't shake it. Weight Watchers told me that their solution worked if I could only be disciplined enough. I believed them. They showed me before and after pictures with disciplined people who had lost weight. The transformation was remarkable. They told me that if those people could do it, I could too. With all their convincing, I rationalized my failure into an understanding of myself. I didn't just do something bad; I was wrong. Guilt is how we feel when we do something wrong, like eating the wrong thing. Shame is a deep, internalized feeling that we are wrong or bad.

The way I see it, the inevitable weight gain that comes from dieting is nothing compared to the accompanying mental and emotional distress. The darkness of shame doesn't have a hold on us around food only—we can experience it in other areas of our life, too. The pervasiveness of feeling wrong or bad can trigger us into a spiral of negative self-talk and painful patterns.

I thought I was doing the right thing by dieting. People around me were also dieting and trying to lose weight. I didn't know I was living in the culture of dieting.

DIET CULTURE

Your workplace may offer a Weight Watchers program. You may have joined with a few colleagues to meal-swap lunches. Your sister's gym follows a paleo diet. Your yogi friends drink their smoothies and eat their kale salads. Friends from college share the ups and downs of intermittent fasting. When you see family around the holidays, they talk about the latest Gwyneth Paltrow clean eating plan. During football season, folks comment on how Tom Brady defies his age by not eating bread. Calories are listed on menus at Panera, and pizza places advertise their keto-friendly menu. I recently saw a nurse practitioner for a rash on my torso, and the nurse asked me to step on the scale. What does my body weight have to do with my skin?

We live in a culture of dieting that is promoted by a variety of systems and groups. Hollywood is just one. We see it in our doctors' offices, schools, workplaces, and gyms. We see it on our social media feeds, on TV commercials, and at sporting events. I can't think of a single place where diet culture doesn't exist. Even New Jersey senator Cory Booker has challenged his Instagram followers to a thirty-day sugar cleanse.

Diet culture is a cultural set of expectations that tells us to eat a certain way to achieve a certain sized body because it will make us a better person. In elementary school, my best friend Heather and I would join her mom for walks before the school bus came. I would go home and eat half a grapefruit for breakfast so I could be thin like the cute girls in my class. If I could be thin like they were, maybe I could also be as pretty and popular as they were. The way I thought about my body and the bodies of my classmates in middle school wasn't something I created in my head; it was a product of diet culture.

Television is the primary way diet culture reinforces the thin body ideal among females. One group of researchers wanted to understand the real impact of how the amount of TV people watch influences women's ideal body size. They selected two villages in Nicaragua, one with minimal access to TV and one urban village with well-established access to TV. Those who watched more TV preferred women in a thinner body. Those who preferred women's bodies to be larger were those who watched TV less.[20]

This is how diet culture spreads its message. Our minds soak up pictures and words of thinness and beauty as truth, pictures and words that are being shown to us without our consent or consideration for a wider variety of body sizes. While I was growing up, I saw pictures and messages on our cable-less TV and in teen magazines. Today, diet culture's messages are sent with far more force and frequency on our social media platforms.

Diet culture is more than just a $72 billion weight loss industry. Diet culture is everywhere. Diet culture instills in us that thin people are more attractive and care about their health because they eat the right foods and work out. And alternatively, diet culture instills in us that people who are overweight don't care about their health; they are lazy and undisciplined.

WEIGHT STIGMA

Early in our marriage, my husband jokingly told me that he didn't care how I dressed as long as I never wore pink sweatpants. I'm not sure what he has against pink sweatpants. I'm pretty sure he likes the color pink, and he owns his fair share of sweatpants. As do I. But pink and sweatpants in his brain don't go together. In my brain, what I heard in his request was, *Don't let yourself go.*

Letting ourselves go is the idea that we stop caring about our bodies because we are so busy with mothering, working, or the dozens of other responsibilities in life that we don't value our own bodies and don't care what we look like anymore. If you've let yourself go and wear pink sweatpants, you've taken yourself down a few notches in your attractiveness and self-care. You may have even gained weight.

While we've been praising thin bodies, we've been putting down fat ones. I'm using the word "fat" as a simple descriptor, like tall or short. While diet culture is a cultural system glorifying dieting, weight stigma involves discriminatory practices toward folks because of their weight and size. Weight stigma includes bullying and fat shaming, and it's most common among family members, classmates, and doctors.[21] Weight stigma impacts people in larger and fat bodies by discriminating against them in the workplace, when they travel, in the educational system, and in the health-care system.[22]

While diet culture is nearly impossible to recognize, weight stigma's cultural oppression is upheld and widely glorified. Discriminating against fat people is often considered funny or seen as a way of doing the overweight person a favor by trying to get them to lose weight. But fat shaming doesn't motivate people to care for their bodies. It only drives them into hiding. When I was bullied about my body on the middle school playground, I wanted to shrink. I wished I was small enough that the boys didn't see me, because if they couldn't, then they wouldn't have teased me the way they did.

To understand weight stigma, we need to understand our history. After all, we weren't born despising fatness; we absorbed the bias that has been well established for centuries. I highly recommend Sabrina Strings' book *Fearing the Black Body*, where she carefully explores how weight stigma has been reinforced for centuries; examines racism, sexism, and classism; and concludes how slim white bodies have been a tool to define and defend the elite white upper class. Weight stigma creates an opposition of one sized body against the other, just like any other form of prejudice and oppression. When there is a supreme sex, age, ability, sexual orientation, and race that lives within us, that hatred and bias doesn't just hurt the oppressed party—it harms ourselves.

It's important to consider the impact of weight stigma on people in overweight and fat bodies, around you and within you. Many of my clients put off going to the doctor because they are worried that their health-care provider is just going to tell them to go on a diet. Discrimination creates massive wear and tear on the body measured by allostatic load. Allostatic load is how the body responds to overload in our nervous system, hormones, and functioning of our hormones. When someone's allostatic load is too high, it puts them at risk for diabetes, heart disease, and hypertension.[23] Shame, bullying, access to equal jobs and pay—all of this erodes our health.

WHY WEIGHT GAIN IS INEVITABLE

Before I started to diet in middle school, I suspect that I was a normal eater. I probably left food on my plate when I was no longer hungry. And I probably had foods I liked to eat and just ate them, without a second thought. I don't have any specific memories of what this was like, probably because eating wasn't a big deal. There was nothing special or worrisome about it. I ate when I was hungry, I stopped when I was full, and I enjoyed eating.

When we start to diet, following external rules and dismissing internal cues, the ease of being with food goes away. We stop feeling relaxed around food and stop trusting our bodies to know how to feed ourselves in a normal way.

When going on a calorie-restricted diet, our bodies respond as if we are in a famine. Our metabolism slows, allowing us to survive with fewer calories. This is brilliant if we were in fact living with food insecurity, but our bodies don't know the difference between lack of food because of circumstances such as war or poverty or because we signed up for Noom. I remind clients that after dieting, thanks to our metabolism and the impact of food restriction, our bodies will in fact gain weight when we eat the same number of calories that we did before we started dieting.

Every body has a unique set point, which is the amount of fat storage and body weight that is optimal for the body to protect itself.

Although set point can't be determined by a formula or in a laboratory, it's estimated that our set point falls within a range of ten to twenty pounds.[24] When your body is below its set point, it will start to defend its set point by:

- Increasing hunger signals, including for a wider variety of foods.
- Reducing fullness signals.
- Slowing metabolism.

This is another reason nearly all dieters gain weight in the long term. Our bodies won't tolerate being at a weight below our set point. Our brain will work with other systems in the body to ensure it comes back to its uniquely predefined weight. Food cravings are one way our body makes sure we eat more. We hear strategies from diet culture on how to manage food cravings, like drink lots of water, chew gum, or eat lower-calorie options. But cravings are just a way our body is doing its job. Trying to minimize these cravings would be like trying to get a dog to not bark or a bird to not fly. It's senseless.

No one can tell you if you're at your set point or not. And it's not a reasonable assumption that folks in larger bodies are above their set point. What we do know is that restrictive diets and intentional weight loss are ineffective at weight loss. In fact, dieting is a predictor of weight gain.[25]

When you allow this to sink in, you'll probably start wondering why anyone ever thinks dieting is a viable solution. Diet culture has drilled into our heads the idea that if we want to lose weight, we need to go on a diet.

The truth is that if you want to lose weight and go on a diet, you need to ask yourself, *How much weight do I plan to gain?*

RISKS THAT OUTWEIGH REWARDS

Following the rules of a diet takes tremendous time and energy, often time and energy that you don't have to spare. When I ask clients how often they are thinking about food and weight loss, they tell me most of the day. It's not just the actions that take a lot of time, like keeping a food journal, meal prepping certain recipes, doing longer workouts, and scouring the internet for motivation, inspiration, and tips to stay on track. It's the headspace dieting takes up that's the most impactful. Worrying about eating the wrong thing, plotting how to avoid certain foods, feeling guilty when you've overeaten, beating yourself up for not having a good day, and then trying to find hope that another dieting solution is out there—it's just a matter of finding it. When dieting isn't a full-time job, what do you get to spend your time and energy on? When you go out to eat with friends, are you able to enjoy the conversation, or do you worry about calories?

It's normal for dieters to be preoccupied with food, have low energy, feel irritable and hangry (hungry and angry at the same time), and lose interest in pleasurable activities. In the Minnesota Starvation Experiment, a landmark study done after World War I to understand the impact of starvation on men in their twenties, it was common for hungry men to lose their sex drive, obsess over recipe books, and get agitated and angry when mealtimes changed. Some of them even licked their plates at the end of their meal. These men were on a 1,600-calorie diet, half their daily calorie intake before the study began.[26]

Considering that many low-calorie diets are under 1,200 calories, the impact on our health is not only understandable, it's expected. One of the biggest predictors of an eating disorder is dieting and pursuing weight loss.[27] In fact, 35 percent of dieters develop eating disordered patterns and 20-25 percent of them progress to having a clinical eating disorder.[28]

Consider some of these diet and weight loss behaviors:

- Stepping on a scale more than once a week to check your body weight.
- Tracking calories, macros, or other measures you eat in a tracking app.
- Joining a commercial weight loss program once or several times.
- Overeating or eating emotionally more than once a week.
- Skip meals or go longer than five hours between meals without eating, despite being physically hungry.
- Exercising intensely after you overeat to burn calories.
- Eliminating a certain food group or avoiding certain foods for weight loss.

For dieters, these are normal activities. Yet these activities are characteristics of a clinical eating disorder. It's estimated that in the United States, 30 million people will suffer from an eating disorder in their lifetime.[29]

Eating disorders are the second most deadly of mental health diseases after opioid addiction.[30] Many people with eating disorders aren't properly diagnosed, and many folks don't get the care or treatment they need.

Dieting, the known and accepted way to fulfill the Promise of thinness, isn't a benign activity. At best, it compromises our health; at worst, it's deadly. I can hear your objection. "Yeah, but. Even though dieting is harmful, being overweight isn't healthy." This statement isn't true. And it's not so simple. I invite you to read some of Ragen Chastein's work as a researcher of weight science, weight stigma, and health care.[31] The research on health and body weight concludes that being overweight causes certain diseases. This isn't always accurate. When examining the research more closely, it's more accurate to conclude that high body weight and disease are correlated. It is possible to be healthy at any body size. Check out The Association of Size Diversity and Health,[32] specifically the principles and framework of Health at Every Size, where you can explore a more holistic and inclusive perspective on weight and health.

A CULTURE OF FEAR

A culture of fear tells us that our bodies are wrong, so we are driven to fix them through dieting.

The Promise packages dieting with hope. We've been explicitly told that dieting is the only solution, but it's the most destructive and damaging behavior we can engage in.

If the strategy of dieting was effective, don't you think women would be liking and appreciating their bodies? Shouldn't we be feeling more confident?

The Promise is based in fear. It's a product of diet culture and weight stigma living inside each of us. We've been taught to fear our bodies, to see them as something that can never measure up. This is why if you and I were in a room with a thousand other women in the United States, and I asked everyone who was satisfied with their body, only one hundred of them would raise their hand. That's right—nine hundred of them would have immediately thought about their height, the size of their hips, the color of their skin, the shape of their nose, or the size of their feet.

All 90 percent of us have been walking around believing that something is wrong with our bodies.[33] We've been carrying this shame around. If we aren't actively trying to change it, we are actively wishing it were different. This is why we diet. This is why we constantly wish to be healthier, leaner, and thinner.

Dieting hasn't led us to a body we can appreciate; it has only disconnected us from it. Your body hasn't been a home you feel welcomed in. When you're dieting, your body is viewed as the enemy. It's too hungry. It craves the wrong foods. It makes you lose control around food and binge. You're disassociated with it. You've disowned it. You're fighting it.

Meanwhile, your body is just trying to keep you healthy and in balance.

When it comes to food restriction and overriding your body's cues for nourishment, your body will win every time. We can't biohack, control, and manipulate our bodies. Our bodies are designed to stay in balance, and when they don't have enough nourishment, they will demand it. And sadly, our diet culture tells us we can override our bodies. Not true. You've been trying to control what can't be controlled.

While dieting, you lose. Not body weight. You lose your health and sanity. And not only that, but the losses are costly. The Promise offers us this costly solution to achieving a thin body. It's just not worth it.

Now that we've examined the ineffective strategy of dieting, let's look at the strategies of waiting, proving, and hiding.

CHAPTER 4

PROVING, HIDING, WAITING

We naturally adapt to uncomfortable situations. Living in New England, my family has acclimated to the occasional snowstorms and bitter temperatures with waterproof insulated snow boots and fleece-lined gloves. Car seat warmers also help. My brother survives the extreme heat of Florida by getting in his outdoor workouts before the sun rises.

Like adapting to extreme weather, trying to fulfill the Promise has made us uncomfortable yet we've grown familiar with this discomfort. Just like bitter cold January temperatures in New Hampshire aren't comfortable, we learn to tolerate them.

I'm suspecting your inner compass knows something is out of whack. That's why you've been drawn to this book. And why you haven't been able to name the discomfort or see a way out. You've been trying to survive strategies to be perfect and it's been wearing you thin, no pun intended.

The Promise impacts every area of our lives, including all our relationships. By trying to fix our bodies to be thin and show up as a perfect version of ourselves, we've been accommodating and acclimating. Just because we can adapt to and tolerate discomfort doesn't make the Promise go away, the same way that stocking up on winter hats or working out at 5:00 a.m. doesn't change the outside thermometer.

To pursue perfection, our strategies have been to wait, prove, and hide. These strategies have a cost to us. There are hundreds if not thousands of strategies you're using to fulfill the Promise, each of which feels normal and routine. We've seen our mothers and grandmothers try to fulfill the Promise with their own strategies. But just because we've been doing things a certain way for generations doesn't mean it's right or in our best interest. I'm going to call out the most obvious strategies so you can discover that, like dieting, you've been paying a price.

But first, I want to share my personal story of waiting, proving, and hiding.

THE PROMISE SOLIDIFIED

When I was a junior in high school, I was living in a perfect storm of family turmoil. My mother and I left my stepfather and my brother to live with her friend Judy up the street. Judy had a modern-day Airbnb, and my mother needed an affordable place for us to live in town so I could continue going to my high school. My stepfather treated me in a way I didn't understand. He didn't yell or slap. He ignored me, rarely even acknowledging my presence or saying my name. I felt invisible. I told friends that we didn't get along. Leaving my childhood home filled me with relief and sadness—to leave my stepfather, we had to leave my brother. I was no longer reminded of being invisible, yet I was missing my brother terribly.

Around the same time, my grandmother was sick with lung cancer. I was especially close to Grammy; her house was like home to me. I spent many weekends sleeping there growing up. She ran a farm, and I would help her milk the goats and pick cucumbers and tomatoes out of her huge vegetable garden. She would make me pancakes on Sunday morning. Watching cancer take over her strong body was devastating. A few weeks before she passed away, I stopped by for a visit. Instead of making me homemade pancakes, she popped a few frozen pancakes into the toaster oven. It was a reckoning that had me sobbing in my mom's borrowed car when I was leaving. The reality of the cancer sank in. She would never be able to make me her homemade pancakes again. Her funeral was held on the same day I was supposed to take the SAT, the standardized test used for college admissions in the United States. When I sat for the test a few weeks later, I could barely focus. I even caught myself dozing off in the middle of the test.

One night, the grief of my grandmother's passing, living in a house that wasn't my home, and missing my younger brother was just too much. While lying in my bed in the basement of Judy's house, I had a huge, almost violent cry. I wasn't just lonely. I was in a tiny row boat and in the middle of a huge storm. I decided right there and then—I was alone. And if it had to be, it was all on me. I was the only one who could take care of me. I didn't need anyone's help.

I made a pact with myself. If your parents weren't there for you like you wished, you may have made a similar pact. As a child, you may not have been able to understand their alcoholism, workaholism, or narcissism. Your parents weren't capable of showing or available to show you the love you wanted or needed, and you clearly got the message. You had to navigate the world on your own.

You may have even developed a story explaining their absence. When you felt alone and wondered why, the answer could have been: I'm not lovable or I'm broken or something is wrong with me. What starts as feeling alone becomes personal. In that perfect storm, I felt my pain and sadness, but I wasn't aware of the meaning I gave it at the time. I wanted to feel loved and accepted. This is when the Promise saves the day. How can we prove to the world that we are in fact lovable and worthy of being cared for? We can be perfect. That's how. We can keep busy. Like I decided to do.

Not surprisingly, I scored very poorly on my SAT but thanked my lucky stars I was accepted to the University of Massachusetts in Amherst after being waitlisted. Stepping onto my college campus in the fall of 1988 felt like a fresh start. The intensity of the storm had waned, and I was a two-and-a-half-hour drive away from the turmoil. There was so much opportunity, and I wanted to take advantage of all of it. After making the dean's list my first semester, something clicked. I realized I could earn acknowledgment and success if I just worked hard enough. I didn't have to be hidden in the basement, ignored by my only father figure and abandoned by my beloved grandmother. I could sit in the driver's seat and take control of my future. This wasn't a casual undertaking; this was serious business. I was determined to prove myself.

After I made the dean's list once, there was no going back. The bar kept creeping higher and higher. What else could I do to earn praise? I transferred into business school where the kids seemed smart and had their act together. I studied with my accounting friends late into the evenings. We focused on getting the best job offers. For a wayward young woman trying to make a place in the world, excelling in academics and business was the solution I needed.

On top of that, I could earn praise by running on a division 1 cross-country team—the epitome of trying to control the uncontrollable. Being on the cross-country team was a way I could keep my body small. A small body was a cute body. A cute body was an attractive body. No matter my natural height and weight, I was trying to make myself as small as possible.

I felt like I never had a spare moment. I would be in awe of some of my friends when they didn't study over the weekend or took a Tuesday afternoon to hang out by the campus pond. I didn't have time to waste, not when I could be doing more. I had such a high bar—after I earned an A, there was another class that required one too. Everyone was cheering me on while I found success. I was praised publicly and privately. Just as I was hooked on Kelly's smile in middle school, I was now hooked on the "atta girls" from the adults in my life. But my striving and proving had a cost.

My emotions were all over the place. I'd have moments of feeling in control and moments of feeling overwhelmed. As I continued piling more and more onto my unstable foundation, I'd frequently break down in tears of despair. *I can't do this,* I'd repeat to myself. I was desperate to be better, do better, and show the world a version of myself that wasn't dumb, broken, and alone.

One time, I saw a therapist on campus. Mr. Therapist sat comfortably in his cushy chair, legs crossed, slouching just enough to tell me he was a bit bored. I mentioned to him some of my recent grades (with pride).

"So?" he said.

"So?" I responded, not sure if I had heard him correctly.

"So? So what?" he clarified.

I was stunned. Why was he brushing off something that was such a big deal to me? He obviously didn't know I was waitlisted. He didn't know that Grammy had recently passed away. He didn't know about my family life. But I don't think it would have even mattered. He could have said, "Oh, Tara. You are so much more than your GPA." But that's not what I heard in his "so what." I heard, "No matter what you do, it's never enough."

I learned to prove myself at a very young age, before I had words or awareness for what I was doing and why I was doing it. I was just trying to measure up to a standard I couldn't even articulate. Without realizing it, I was hiding behind a perfect version of myself. I didn't know the real me. I only knew the woman who was determined to be lovable and acceptable. And I waited, all right. Happiness wasn't something I could enjoy, and success wasn't something I could acknowledge for myself. I'd have to wait until I was good enough.

When I'd refuse to let myself eat lunch in the dining hall, I didn't call it dieting. I wasn't following rules; I was taking advantage of opportunities. If I could just do enough and eat less, I'd feel successful and happy. The Promise was already instilled in me in 1990. It took me almost thirty years to understand what was really happening.

I'LL PROVE IT TO YOU

We celebrate people's grit and kindness because they are positive attributes that help us get ahead and be successful. This makes proving difficult to detect because hard work and prioritizing others' needs are good things.

Did you grow up in one of those families where your mom cooked dinner, but was the last to sit down at the dinner table and the first to get up to clear the dishes? Even though time has passed, have times really changed? Our internal wiring and patterns that have passed through each generation to the point that caring for our partners, parents, and children is assumed. Women are natural-born caretakers, whether we ask for it or not, and whether we like it or not. This is why professions that primarily care for others, like teachers, nurses, health-care workers, house cleaners, and restaurant servers, are dominated by women. Proving ourselves as a daughter, wife, or mother means we prioritize our loved ones' needs before our own.

This is another expectation placed on us. We've been trained to do this, and our own needs rarely get acknowledged by others or ourselves. This is not always true of men. I saw my stepfather work hard. He would grumble about how busy his day was because he barely had a moment to stop. And then I'd see him watching TV on the couch after his workday ended. My mother worked full time as a nurse at our local hospital. When she got home from work, she was in charge of getting dinner on the table. I'm sure she didn't have a moment to stop during her workday either.

As a working mother, I never felt like my day could officially end. Kids needed to be picked up from daycare or school. Groceries needed to be gathered, food needed to be prepared, and the house needed to be cleaned. What still amazes me to this day, as my role and responsibilities have evolved over two decades of motherhood, is that I always assumed this role without question or resistance, even though it left me exhausted, overwhelmed, and often feeling like I sucked at everything else I was doing in my life.

When we prove, we dismiss our own needs to prioritize the needs of others. The needs I'm talking about are basic. Sleep. Nourishment. Downtime. Outside time. While pursuing the Promise, taking time for ourselves can be seen as selfish. While we've been conditioned to be caretakers, what's really happening is we've joined a labor camp that doesn't allow for women to acknowledge that we have basic needs that are a priority.

Boundaries in the workplace can have the same flavor. Work demands come before your own health and well-being. Are you hungry at lunch but forgo a meal to meet a deadline? Do you work well into the evening despite your exhaustion? A client shared her feelings on exhaustion with me while working a demanding full-time job and running her household. "I'll rest when I retire," she'd say. This is how we wait. We can't prove ourselves and rest at the same time.

When we need to prove ourselves, we can never do enough. There is always more to do when we are doing the jobs of several people. When we sacrifice sleep, time with friends and family, and other basic needs, we aren't chasing the goal—we're chasing the feeling that leaves us knowing we've done good and that we are worthy and esteemed. But perfection never allows for good enough. We keep trying to find more time and energy to prove ourselves, yet even the accolades of others don't fulfill us.

When we put our needs last, we are living in a state of deprivation and tolerating it. We rob ourselves of life's pleasures because we believe we always need to be sacrificing.

SEE THE PERFECT ME

Hiding is another way we fulfill the Promise. When we can't prove our perfection, we hide the parts of us that we don't measure up. The trouble is that by hiding a part of you, you hide other parts too. When I taught yoga, new yogis always wanted to set up their mats at the back of the class. They didn't want to risk being seen as newbies in front of more experienced yogis. I get that. One could say that's a reasonable approach to starting something new. But sitting in the back of a classroom so the teacher doesn't call on you could be one way to hide. It doesn't mean that's wrong or bad; the larger question is whether you feel in your bones that you deserve to be in the room and that your presence matters.

When I run groups around intuitive eating and body image, I gently remind my students of this. They don't have to say anything or share a word, but when they show up, they have an impact. A woman in the group may be sharing a story about body shame for the first time, and when another person is there to hear it, she heals. But when people hide because they don't believe in the value of their presence, their contribution will never be felt. That is what we all miss because of hiding.

I was in math class in middle school when the whole class was struggling with a problem. Mrs. Doyle, my teacher, was being patient, but I also could sense her frustration. She called on me. "Tara, you know this answer." I did have an answer, but I wasn't willing to raise my hand.

What if I was wrong? Could I risk the embarrassment? Raising my hand and letting the class know the answer with confidence wasn't my instinctual response. It was safer to not be wrong, to not stand out, to not take risks. I'd rather not be seen than be seen as wrong. We start engaging with the Promise at a very early age.

It turns out I wasn't alone. Reshma Saujani, founder and CEO of Girls Who Code,[34] shared a common experience of coding instructors among middle school girls and boys during her keynote talk at the Bryant University's Women's Summit in 2019.[35] After a period of time, the girls had a blank piece of paper and the boys had their code written. When asked, the girls said they didn't write an answer because they weren't confident it would be correct. They would rather offer no answer than a wrong one. The boys, however, knew that making mistakes was part of learning, and they were willing to do it.

Our young girls already know how to hide their answers out of risk that they will be wrong. The Promise has already conditioned them to only show the perfect version of themselves in the classroom, or else risk being called out as wrong or stupid.

We can also hide behind the version of ourselves we think we need to be. As I mentioned, for years when I was running my accounting consulting firm, I'd straighten my curly hair when I went to my clients' offices. Just like thinness is a requirement for success, I believed looking professional was too. In my mind, curly hair was unruly and wild. I needed to show the world my hair was tame and smooth. I'd shower the night before and wash my hair so it could dry overnight. Then I'd wake up extra early to straighten every section of hair. It would take me anywhere between thirty and forty-five minutes. But this was the price I needed to pay to show my clients that I had my shit together.

Can you see how exhausting hiding can be? It runs the gamut, from how we wear our hair and how we dress to how we speak up to share what's on our mind. The Promise has taught us to show the world an acceptable, perfect, and thin version of ourselves. If we can't be that, we've been hiding.

The sad part is that you may be so accustomed to hiding that you don't know who the real you is. Who are you when you don't need to be perfect? How can you show up when you don't need to look and perform a certain way? It's sad, but it's also a way we protect ourselves from judgment and blame. Hiding is generally a shameful response. When we believe we are bad or wrong, of course we don't want anyone to see us. So, hiding and trying to be small is a way we think we can feel safe.

We can also hide behind what we do. Remember the college student I mentioned who told me how she and her roommates were always trying to outdo each other by being the most stressed? They didn't necessarily do this intentionally or overtly. But when we are busy, we need to show the world how productive and in demand we are. Being busy or a workaholic is a way to show the world a perfect version of yourself. It's not the real you, just the you that you think you need to be.

When I was one of three facilitators-in-training with my teaching mentors at a yoga retreat in Mexico, I was filled with self-doubt. There I was, a fairly new yoga teacher, among forty or so other yoga teachers, the majority of whom had much more experience than I did.

Each day, one of my mentors and I would pair up in a group of other yoga teachers and offer them feedback while they taught. I was desperate to be the perfect yoga teacher facilitator, someone everyone liked and looked up to. I wanted the other teachers to look up to me and value what I had to offer. I asserted my knowledge so I looked smart. I delivered feedback in a way that wouldn't piss off or hurt anyone.

All my actions were clouded by a desire to be liked. I was trying to give them a version of me that I thought they'd like and approve of. Everything I did felt forced. I felt like a little puppy running up to every teacher seeking their love and attention. This wasn't freedom; this was captivity. I knew I was trying too hard, but I didn't know how to stop myself. I couldn't just be who I was; I needed to be someone better.

When we try to make those around us like us, whether consciously or unconsciously, it takes a lot of freakin' effort and energy. I was so consumed with wondering whether these yoga teachers liked me that not getting their approval—or worse, noticing their indifference—was devastating.

Pursuing perfection means we have to show the world the good girl version of ourselves that people like. The Promise has taught us to be a good girl. Good girls don't speak up, and they don't speak about controversial issues that may upset people. Good girls don't get angry, and they go out of their way to be nice. We hide behind our good girl facade. But it's painful to contort ourselves into someone else. If I could sum up in one word how I felt in Mexico, it would be *invisible*.

THE WAITING PLACE

Dr. Seuss, the famous children's author, wrote a book that's given to many high school and college students when they graduate called *Oh, the Places You'll Go!* It shares all the right inspiration along with the pitfalls people will encounter when they go out into the world to be their unique selves. Dr. Seuss warns us of the Waiting Place, the place where people are just waiting. They are waiting for the pot to boil or their hair to grow or the bus to come or the phone to ring. This is a "useless" place, he warns, one that we all need to escape from as quickly as possible.

I don't disagree with Dr. Seuss, and I'm sure you don't either. Waiting doesn't get us anywhere; it just makes us waste time. But that's where the Promise is so deceptive. The Promise gives us, in theory, good reason to wait. If we haven't fulfilled our end of the Promise, we haven't yet earned the success and the happiness we've been believing will come our way. Waiting isn't something we see as bad or wrong, it's just that we haven't done our job yet. We need more time. We need to work harder and do more. We need to find the right diet and make sure it really sticks this time. You may not see yourself as waiting because you've been busy proving. This gives you the illusion that you're closer to fulfilling the Promise than you really are. With every project you complete or sales deal you close, with every salad and extra-sweaty workout at the gym, you're getting closer and closer.

Let me be clear: we should not confuse waiting with needing time to gain experience, to practice, and to learn. Patience and persistence are respectable qualities—hence the saying that "all good things come to those who wait." A new college graduate will not land the corner office after a few months or even years. A rock band needs to produce plenty of songs and take years honing their skills before they can produce a chart topper. When I started swimming, it took me a lot of practice to work on my stroke and flip turn until swimming didn't feel laborious anymore. Everyone needs time to do these things before they gain some level of mastery. But that's not waiting.

Waiting has been woven into the fabric of our society as a manipulation tool. Kids are told they need to be good girls and boys for Santa to come on Christmas. A s I previously mentioned, you can detect waiting by its "if-then" or "when-then" formula: If I lose ten pounds, then I'll buy that cute pair of jeans. If I get to my goal weight, then I'll go on my dream vacation. When I fit into my skinny jeans, then I'll start dating again. When I finish this high-profile project, then I'll ask for a raise. When the house is clean, then I'll relax.

According to a study published in the *Harvard Business Review*, women will apply for jobs only when they meet 100 percent of the qualifications. However, men will apply for jobs when they meet only 60 percent of the qualifications.[36] When asked why, women shared that they didn't believe they would be hired if they didn't meet all the qualifications; they took the qualifications as true guidelines and wanted to respect the process. They didn't want to apply and fail. Waiting is deceiving. "I'll apply for that job when I'm fully qualified" sounds like a reasonable statement until we consider it under the lens of perfectionism. That's when we hear, "If I'm perfect, I'll go after my dream job."

The truth is, we can have all those things now without needing to change a single thing.

Underneath waiting lies our desires and dreams. Most people are waiting to some degree. My husband is a few years from retirement, and he's definitely waiting for it. He jokes that he'll be making dinner for us most nights because he'll have time to be in the kitchen instead of running from meeting to meeting and call to call. But right now, my husband makes us lovely fish dinners and homemade pasta dishes on the weekends. Sure, he's waiting for an open schedule and the freedom from work, but he hasn't put his life on hold until he's no longer working.

The Promise teaches us that we need to be more. And this standard rises—each time we meet one milestone, we must set another goal so we can try to achieve more. When one business wasn't enough for me to feel successful, I needed another. And another. But no number of businesses would provide that feeling of success when I believed I wasn't enough. How do you know you've been waiting? You keep holding on to a fantasy that your life will be better when something changes. You wait because you don't accept things just as they are. You also feel exhausted because while you've been waiting, you've been proving and hiding.

The Promise makes us wait to experience enjoyment. That's why exploring our personal pleasure is the ultimate act of rebellion. The Promise and its underlying cultural narratives keep us from doing this. If you enjoy sex, you may feel guilty about it because you're considered a temptress, someone who's out of control and dangerous. You also may feel guilty for loving to eat and enjoying food. However, allowing yourself pleasure is a way for you to know yourself. We need fun, joy, and happiness in our lives. It's part of being human. It's not our fault that we've been conditioned to deprioritize ourselves, but no one else will prioritize us—we are the only ones who can.

We've been fulfilling the Promise by waiting, proving, and hiding, which has left us feeling stuck, exhausted, and frustrated. Why haven't we seen all this chaos and discomfort before now? Why have we been putting up with all this bullshit? The answer is simple.

The Promise has given us the illusion of safety.

That's why it's a Promise. We've been believing that all our sacrifices and efforts will get us somewhere. The fantasy of a better life offers us hope and comfort. It's masterful in its deception. If we could have strategized and rationalized our way out of the Promise, we would have. But the Promise's illusion of safety doesn't rely on our rational mind; it sits deep inside us. In fact, it's wired into our nervous system. That's right, the Promise lives inside our bodies.

CHAPTER 5

THE ILLUSION

We've been trying to fulfill the Promise with the belief that when we do, we will feel happier, more successful, and more attractive. This success will offer us a sense of belonging, a sense that we are lovable and good enough. Even though we've been under an illusion of what the Promise offers us, the Promise hooks us on measuring ourselves based on external standards created by the patriarchy, a cultural system that upholds the power of men at the exclusion and harm of women.

While engaging in the Promise, we've been playing a lose-lose game. The standards of thinness and perfection can never be met. Ever. Which means we will fail and remain under attack. Day to day, we've acclimated to an environment of threat. These threats have often been subtle and normalized, but we've registered them as threats nonetheless. To understand how this interpretation of threat is working, we need to explore the fundamentals of how our nervous system works to keep us safe.

OUR PROTECTION MECHANISM

Humans and animals have a complex, internal set of wiring designed to maintain safety. It's called the nervous system. The nervous system is always on alert, running behind the scenes, mostly without our awareness.

In high school, I was crossing the street in the middle of the day when a group of men started catcalling at me. I was startled, and while my mind was trying to process what was happening, my nervous system immediately kicked in. My heart rate jumped. I started to sweat. I felt a pit of energy in the bottom of my belly. All I wanted to do was run away and hide. This was my nervous system working to keep me safe. The nervous system is constantly asking, "Am I safe?" Even if those men intended no harm with their calls, my nervous system determined I was under threat.

When I started my yoga studio and my coaching business part time, Brian, my business coach, highly encouraged me to write a weekly newsletter. So I did. I'd often share something personal, explain how yoga had impacted my life, or write about my relationship with food. When it was time for me to send the newsletter to the people on my email list, I'd get a massive cold sore. When I started to learn about how our bodies react to trauma, my cold sores finally made sense.

Sharing my writing made me feel vulnerable and judged by my readers. At some unconscious level, it was putting my body under stress. When we can't process the stress, our body lets us know. My cold sore indicated that feeling so exposed was unsafe.

When our nervous system senses danger, it tells our brain that we aren't safe and therefore need to protect ourselves by fighting, fleeing, freezing, or pleasing.

The fight response shows up as anger or frustration. Little things may set you off. When your teenager asks you where his keys are (because he's always misplacing them), you snap at him. When your partner breathes the wrong way, you feel so annoyed you want to scream. Your senses are heightened, and you're acutely scanning and assessing your environment for threat. When we are triggered into the fight response because we feel judged or criticized, our natural reaction is to prove ourselves. Proving yourself is hundreds of mini fight responses happening repeatedly because of the fear that you're not enough. Your fight response to this fear means you go above and beyond on a project, get into the office early before the rest of your team, and refuse to let anything fall through the cracks. Proving is a response to your internal fight.

I'm sure you're familiar with the flight response, but you've likely been calling it anxiety, stress, or worry. When your body is in a flight response, it's common to repeat the same thought. For example: How am I going to get this done? What if I'm late? What if this doesn't work out the way I need it to? Your shoulders may tense, and you may feel a pressure in your chest. With the flight response, your focus and energy often leaves the present to focus on future threats. When you're in a flight response, you can leave physically or check out emotionally or mentally. You're essentially hiding.

The freeze response kicks in after your body has activated the flight-or-fight response. Freeze happens when flight or fight doesn't seem to keep you safe enough. When your body freezes, you feel detached, depressed, and ashamed. This is the state of stuckness, when it's hard to move forward. When animals freeze, they play dead, hoping their predator will leave them alone and move on. It's generally the last resort when a deer knows it can't fight a bear or run from a cougar. The freeze response can feel like darkness and hopelessness. When we are in a freeze response, we are waiting. We may say to ourselves, *I can't do this right now.*

Pleasing or fawning is unique to humans. It makes sense that if you live with someone who drinks or has a bad temper you try to make the situation safer by doing whatever you can to pacify that person. That person creates a threat, and by pleasing them, you're trying to make yourself safer. But it doesn't need to be violence you're trying to protect yourself from. We can fawn over wanting to be loved or wanting to avoid judgment. Those who fawn or please are masterful at anticipating the nuances of making an environment safer. Like when your mother asks you for a favor that requires moving mountains, you do it anyway because saying no means she will be disappointed in you—and that doesn't feel safe. When we please others, we forsake our own needs and have no boundaries or self-interests.

Our nervous system responses drive the strategies we've been engaging in to fulfill the Promise. When we get triggered into fight, we prove and try to work our way back to what we believe is a safe place. When we're triggered into flight, we hide. When we're triggered into freeze or please, we wait and feel stuck.

When our body is threatened and seen as a problem that triggers a nervous system reaction, it's nearly impossible to be connected to our body. It is on too high alert for us to feel grounded.

Our body is a power source. Without the connection

to our body, we don't know how to experience joy, success, pure delight, and happiness. We also don't know how to fully experience sorrow, anger, and grief. Without a connection to our bodies, we are disconnected from our true selves.

THE ILLUSION OF CONTROL

Early in my CPA career, I sat in a large auditorium among hundreds of other accountants in my office for an afternoon of continuing education training, which meant we were getting updates on the latest accounting rulings. It couldn't be more boring. So I planned something much more exciting: my workout and eating plan for the next month.

My optimism was tangible. I had visions of my clothes fitting better, of myself happily eating a salad for lunch and adding a few extra miles to my runs. I was hooked on the fantasy that when I lost weight, my whole life would click into place. I'd feel better, look better, and be a better person. I'd also feel more worthy of my professional success. By dropping a dress size, I could celebrate my new promotion because I wouldn't just have the title—I'd also *look* like a successful woman.

Engaging in the fantasy of weight loss gives us an illusion of control. Even if the scale doesn't budge, we are at least trying to drop the weight. And trying feels better than giving up and letting ourselves go. When we keep trying, we convince ourselves we are making progress and that someday, our dreams may become reality. Diet harder. Prove more. Chase that sense of control that comes from doing the "right" thing.

I can still recall my excitement when I joined Weight Watchers. It was like I had just been handed a newly sharpened pencil and got to do some math problems on my blank piece of paper. I love the certainty of numbers, and knowing how they all fit together gave me a sense of satisfaction by answering one thing: Have I done it right?

Not surprisingly, the Weight Watchers program in the early 2000s was designed for a numbers enthusiast like myself. I logged into its website and entered my weight, age, height, activity level, and how much weight I wanted to lose. Its calculations told me how much I was "allowed" to eat each week. A few times a day, I'd log into the website and record what I ate and how much I exercised. Everyday, I was an active participant in my weight, which gave me both the focus and distraction I needed to soothe myself.

Diets create faux safety because they give us a sense of control, which we may not feel around food. Even though the promise of the diet (weight loss) and the act of dieting (trying to control) gives us safety, the sense of control is always fleeting. No human can safely withstand food restriction without a stress or duress response. As I mentioned earlier, if dieting offered you real control, you'd always feel at peace around food.

Another way we try to stay in control is by not making mistakes. When I started working in corporate accounting, I realized quickly this was the measure of my success. But because I wasn't making mistakes, everyone around me didn't notice or praise the work I was doing. Success meant that employees were paid the right amount, financial reports were flawless, and deadlines were always met. Things were going well when I didn't draw any attention to myself or my department because I was running things perfectly. One of the biggest threats when you feel unsafe is having the spotlight shine on you.

Because there was nothing to praise, I could comfortably live in the dimness. When proving ourselves, we are doing our damnedest to avoid criticism. Striving for perfection and doing our jobs flawlessly means we are protecting ourselves from the criticism. This gives the illusion that we are keeping ourselves safe from being outcast as not smart or capable enough.

THE ILLUSION OF BELONGING

When we fulfill others' expectations of us, people around us who hold those expectations are happy with us. For most women, being good is about being nice, maternal, pretty, thin, and taking care of everyone around us. We've tried to play this part as a good girl, wife, worker, sister, daughter. But duty has a price, and when the bar that's been set for us has no limit, nothing we do will ever be good enough. And when we don't measure up, we assume we've done something wrong.

This is why women have been called people pleasers and why they may have a hard time saying no or setting personal boundaries. We are trying to fulfill what's expected of us. What happens when we don't? We feel like we don't belong.

When pursuing perfection, our prison bars are built with guilt. Guilt has a way of disguising itself as a do-gooder. We convince ourselves that we need a healthy dose of guilt to keep ourselves in check. Without a bit of guilt, we would go rogue, eating Snickers bar after Snickers bar. We'd lay in bed all day. We'd not show up at our jobs, not make dinner for our families, and not fold a single piece of clothing. This is how we know the Promise is instilled in us. No one has to tell us the rules because our internal, guilt-filled compass keeps us on track. Guilt is what keeps us proving. Proving makes us feel safe because we are under the illusion we belong.

Feeling like you're obligated to make someone else happy or feel better is burdensome. The Promise has left us feeling empty and desiring to feel needed, and when we feel needed, we feel a sense of belonging. The only thing that could be worse is doing something for others and feeling taken advantage of or not appreciated.

There is a tipping point. We give and give, prioritize others' needs and desires, and placate, but then there is a moment when we have nothing left to give. And then something will push us to the brink. A snarky comment from our teenager. A fight between our children. Another request from our boss. And that's it. We lose it. I can recall times when a rage would wash over me, and I'd turn into a screaming lunatic. My whole house would know I was upset. My friend Tracy is the opposite. She bottles everything inside and goes quiet, building a wall to distance herself emotionally and physically from her kids and husband.

There is no end to what we do for the people because we are prioritizing our need to please others ahead of our own need for rest and peace. Wondering why you feel so angry? So resentful? So overwhelmed? Of course we want to feel appreciated and not taken advantage of. We've trained those around us to expect that we will take care of them. Some of this is perfectly reasonable, but when we lose our shit or shut down, it's gone too far.

This trap is easy to step into because it has unclear boundaries. After all, we are taking on the responsibility of several people simultaneously. Who can do that? Doesn't it make sense we want something in return? Of course. But the perfect woman doesn't ask for anything; she works with a smile. Meanwhile, the anger brews. It shows up when we start banging pots and pans in the kitchen. When we go to bed without speaking to our family or pick a fight with our partner.

It's easy to blame those around us for not making us feel appreciated. Truth be told, no one is making us get dinner on the table, clean the kitchen, fold the clothes, book the travel arrangements, sign the kids up for Little League, or help sell raffle tickets for the school fundraisers. It's the Promise that's driving us. And that drive for perfection only makes us feel like a doormat.

The Promise offers us an illusion of belonging and only disconnects us from those we love and those who love us. When we're trying to be that perfect person for everyone, we lose ourselves and we lose our shit. We go back and forth between feeling guilty and feeling pissed off.

THE ILLUSION OF PROGRESS

In Greek mythology, Sisyphus was a really bad dude. He was a murderer, trickster, and seducer—he even seduced his niece in an attempt to overthrow his brother's reign. He was determined to claim power at any cost. He certainly deserved to be punished—and he was. Zeus sentenced him to an eternity of pushing a massive boulder up a steep mountain, only to have it tumble down every time he reached the top. The Greek gods knew how devastating it was to work tirelessly at something only to have to do it again and again, without ever making progress and being acknowledged. For his crimes, Sisyphus could never declare victory when he reached the top of the mountain. And he could never give up.

Like Sisyphus, you and I know the maddening frustration of being driven toward something with no reward. We've all engaged in endless, tireless undertakings that steals our sanity, health, joy, and peace of mind. Unlike Sisyphus, we haven't done anything wrong to receive our sentence. We were born women, wanting success and happiness. We didn't see any other viable options besides trying to be perfect. No one warned us or said, "Stop! Don't waste your time trying to lose those ten pounds," or "You've got nothing to prove! Prioritize your health first." Not only did we not receive any warnings or understand the consequences of our choices, but our trusted role models have also been engaged in the Promise. This makes us believe we've been doing the right thing.

We've been under the illusion that progress means we are closer to fulfilling the Promise. When we believe that fulfilling the Promise will give us what we've been looking for, we stay committed to the strategies we've been given. Small steps forward can give us that sense of accomplishment: Yes! I'm on the right track. I need to just keep going. The illusion of progress convinces us that we're close to the finish line, but there is no finish line.

Sisyphus can't stop pushing his boulder, but we can stop engaging in the Promise. Turning our attention away from it isn't as easy as turning our car around and driving in a new direction. The Promise lives in our hearts in the form of our aspirations. And fulfilling it hasn't been a casual undertaking. It's been an all-in, fully encompassing endeavor that takes up an enormous amount of space in our brains and hearts. The Promise has been embedded in how we spend our time and money.

The Promise is a way for us to fix ourselves, which distracts our focus, energy, time, and money. Just like there is always a diet to buy, there is always a self-help program that will teach us how to fix ourselves. But it's the Promise that needs fixing, not you. I guarantee that if you were to share with me what's really driving you nuts right now and keeping you up at night, I can point out the Promise as the cause. How you've been engaging in the Promise is what's creating your problems. It's not you.

It's not just swapping an hour for calorie counting and an hour for creating a business plan. When you're not dieting and proving, you get to focus on life-giving, self-esteem-enhancing activities. Your reclaimed energy pays you back tenfold and keeps building your strength, resilience, and sense of self.

YOUR BODY, YOUR CHOICE

Consider a ladder of privilege and power. White able-bodied men sit at the top. White women sit directly under their white male counterparts. What's the best way to make sure the status quo isn't disrupted? Distract them. Make them focus on something else. Make them feel insecure and uncertain. Threaten them and offer them a false sense of security. The Promise takes the most privileged group of women—the white, cisgender, heterosexual, and able-bodied—and treats them like a threat. This group arguably is the most dangerous because it has the privilege of education, wealth, and access to power.

The Promise is delivering. It's promising that we will be disconnected from our bodies, distracted from what's most important to us, and feeling defeated and disempowered. And dieting harder and proving more only harms our health and sense of self-worth. The Promise has been delivered, all right. It's an essential component of the patriarchy to ensure that women stay disempowered so men's power is not threatened.

Now that we know that dieting isn't effective, and trying to be perfect is really only the act of trying to be someone else, we can see that engaging in both of these strategies takes our time and attention away from what really matters.

When you're exhausted, obsessing about food, and feeling like crap because you just stepped on the scale, are you able to fully engage in your life? To pursue your passions and dreams? To trust in yourself and your abilities?

Over time, I acclimated to sending newsletters and sharing my blogs, videos, and podcast episodes. I still have those little cringy experiences at times, but thanks to my ability to soothe myself, practices I'll be sharing with you in chapter 6, my system is no longer under duress.

The good news is you're walking around in the solution. Your body holds the answers. You have resources, you just haven't been taught how to use them. Now that you have a basic understanding of your nervous system's role in safety, you can start to see the uncomfortable patterns in a new light. Instead of beating yourself up for them, know that this is your body's way of trying to protect yourself. Your body's signals are a welcomed indicator, a check engine light, letting you know that your body needs attention.

The Promise teaches us to see our body as an object, an object that needs to look a certain way. I shared in chapter 3 that 95 percent of women are dissatisfied with their bodies. This is why. When our body becomes an object, we become the observer of that object. This becomes the way most people learn to be with their body: as an observer. As an observer and ultimately a critic, we naturally see our bodies as bad or wrong. Who wants to connect with something that's bad or wrong? Feeling this way about our body makes it hard to want to live inside it.

Untethering yourself from the Promise means that you need to go to the body, listen to it, and honor how all these mechanisms are working perfectly for your well-being. It can be difficult to break yourself from this cycle. But now you understand that this is a choice you get to make.

You are fully capable of creating your own internal safety and accepting yourself as you are. But first, you need to break free from the Promise.

CHAPTER 6

BREAKING THE PROMISE

We've been brilliant in our resourcefulness. Our brains are masterful at figuring out how to solve a problem and come up with a solution. You and I have gone after our dreams and our desires in the best way we've known how. We were born into this world and boom, our primal instincts kicked in. We figured out how to not just survive but thrive in a culture that doesn't have our backs.

Now that you understand how your nervous system works, you know that you've engaged in strategies to keep you safe. But that safety isn't real. Now, it's time to remove the facade so you can create something real for yourself.

Don't expect to overhaul the Promise's impact on your life in a day, a week, or even a month. And don't expect to undo it in all areas of your life immediately. Before you move toward something new, you need to deliberately disengage yourself from the status quo. To do this, we can't try to fix or improve the Promise of the Thin and Perfect. The Promise is built on oppression, bias, stigma, and sexism; fixing it would only be validating it. It needs to be burned down, not reinvented. We have to completely detach ourselves from it, for the same reasons that we don't enter a healthy relationship with a new partner until we've closed the door on our past romantic relationships.

In this chapter, I'm going to arm you with exercises so you can break free from the Promise. Grab a journal and a pen. It's time to journal. Take your time. You can't rip the Promise off like a Band-Aid, but with some practice and persistence, you'll free yourself from it.

CONNECTING TO YOUR POWER SOURCE

The relationship you have with your body is one of your most important relationships. It is your power source. Connecting with it will change your life. Being cut off from it turns us into unrecognizable beings.

The Promise has us turned against our power source. We've been so busy judging, controlling, and fixing our bodies to make them acceptable, we haven't had a chance to partner with our own internal power. Depending on your age, you may not even remember what it's like to partner with your body and feel completely supported and loved just being in your own skin.

As you begin this journey of self-discovery and disconnecting from the Promise, you won't be thinking about who you should be; instead, you'll listen to the whispered signals that have been vibrating inside you since the day you were born. You've been severed from them. You didn't think these signals were important. You were never taught to respect and honor this wisdom. Yet your source is something you've been walking around in, sleeping in, and living in.

You may be thinking, *That sounds great, Tara. I love the idea. How the hell do I do that?* I'd be asking the same question if I were you. This process isn't about checking something off a to-do list. You don't need to rush your way through it. That's how we operate under the Promise. Let's start with this simple exercise.

EXERCISE

- First, acknowledge the wisdom inside you. Even if you haven't heard her yet, believe she's in there somewhere. Be willing to suspend any disbelief.

- Next, think of your body like a long-lost friend or a childhood playmate.
- Spend a few moments throughout the day engaging with your body. You can do this by noticing sensations. I know this is a simple exercise, but don't let its simplicity elude you. When you notice your breath, you are becoming aware of an energy force that moves in and out of your body.
- Place your left hand over your heart. Place your right hand over your left hand.
- Sit up tall. Close your eyes.
- Take some long, deep breaths.
- What do you notice? Does anything change after the first few breaths?
- Pay attention to your breath to remind yourself that you're living in your body and your body offers you the comfort, security, and wisdom you've been missing.

LIVING IN YOUR BODY

Embodiment is a multidimensional way you inhabit your body. You can observe someone to discover clues around what they are embodying. If their shoulders are rounded and they are looking down, you may sense they are sad or discouraged. If you are in a meeting with Sally and she's light, bright, and bubbly, it's safe to assume she's embodying passion and joy.

Although embodiment can be observed in some cases, it's really about what's happening for the person inside. Using awareness, intention, feelings, and our way of relating to certain things or objects, embodiment helps us tune in to ourselves but also purposely change the direction in which we'd like to travel.

Embodiment tells us about our history—after all, our body holds memories, energies, and patterns that can be subtly or not so subtly reflected in the way we walk through this world. But more importantly, embodiment is a practice that allows us to change how we show up in our lives. Without it, we can't be truly seen.

EXERCISE

The first step to embodiment is just becoming aware of your body. What do you feel? What do you notice? What's happening with your energy?

To do this, you need to be able to notice physical sensations like heat, warmth, coolness, tension, lightness, expansion. Your body is reflecting what's going on for you internally—how you are feeling and what you're thinking. To reflect and feel the true version of yourself, you must partner with your body.

Say the word "love" to yourself out loud a few times. Notice how your body reacts. Your chest, belly, and throat are common areas where you'll notice sensation. When I say love to myself, I can feel an expansion in my chest.

Now, say the word "hate" to yourself out loud a few times. Notice how your body reacts to this word. Do you notice a difference?

You can choose other words like "gratitude," "grace," "judgment," or "rejection." You may notice your body respond right away, or you may need to do this exercise a few times until you notice its reaction. Be patient with yourself.

When I started practicing this exercise, I'd use it when making decisions: Would my body like a banana or yogurt for a snack? Am I excited about working with the potential client I'd just had a clarity call with? Now, I notice my body's response quickly enough to know what's a "yes" and what's a "no."

EXERCISE

To feel safe, you need to let your mind and body arrive in the present moment. You must transition from your fearful state, when your mind goes to either the past or the future. There are many ways to create a safe container.

Practice a few of these suggestions to find out which ones feel best for you. Then incorporate them into your daily routine.

- Practice intentional breathing.
- Sit quietly for a minute or two and notice the sensations in your body.
- Smell an essential oil.
- Walk outside in nature.
- Dance.
- Draw.
- Journal about something that's on your mind.

TREATING YOUR BODY WITH RESPECT

When your body doesn't need fixing, you don't need to lose weight to feel safe. Until now, fixing your body was a survival technique. Going forward, you can care for your body deeply, out of respect. You can eat foods you love and nourish your body. You can move your body in a way that feels joyful.

When you don't need to lose weight, it means you can stop dieting. I highly recommend intuitive eating as a way for you to stop dieting and start connecting to and caring for your body. Intuitive eating is a self-care practice that allows you to tune in to what you need and treat your body with great respect. In addition, I subscribe to the health-at-every-size approach, which means that no matter what size body you live in, you can support your health without needing to diet or lose weight.

Respecting your body also requires you to recognize the external systems of diet culture and weight stigma, which I shared in chapter 3. Once you notice them, you can't unsee them. Weight loss commercials will start to enrage you. Your eyes will immediately be drawn to words like "clean" and "healthy" on food packaging. You'll overhear someone comment on someone else's weight loss and dream of a world where our bodies aren't on display for anyone's comments, whether praise or criticism.

Like me, you may dream of a world where your body size is no one else's business, and you can focus on who you are as a person and can feel safe to live in your body regardless of its size. When you see a person in a large body squeeze into an airplane seat, instead of judging them for their body, you could be curious. What's it like for them to sit so uncomfortably? Maybe they are going on vacation and can't even relax, or they are going to a loved one's funeral and just want comfort.

When your body isn't a problem, how do you treat it? First, you can stop looking for a diet and start to heal from dieting. It may take years to unlearn all the ways you've been dieting and food restricting. The first principle of intuitive eating is to reject the diet mentality. I shared in chapter 2 that dieting only guarantees long-term weight gain. But actively rejecting dieting means you're able to examine your food rules and no longer follow them. Second, you can honor your hunger, another principle of intuitive eating. Learning what hunger feels like for you and nourishing yourself when your body is hungry will be a game-changer. So many people feel anxious and preoccupied with food thoughts because they are hungry. When you start eating regular meals and snacks when you're hungry, food won't be on your mind all the time.

Can you sense the shift here? By disconnecting from the Promise, you're going to respect instead of reject your body.

EXERCISE

Consider these journaling questions:

- What has your body been asking for?
- What is the one thing you can do now to offer it what it needs? Our body is always keeping us in balance. To do this, it often reacts in ways that are unwanted. For example, you may overeat if you haven't been eating enough. You may feel exhausted when you're not getting enough rest. You may feel resistant to starting a new project when you need more downtime and space.

- How can you reframe signals from your body as it shares its wisdom with you instead of assuming your body is wrong?
- What can you appreciate about your body?

FEELING YOUR EMOTIONS

In addition to connecting to our power source and treating our body with respect, we must also learn to feel our emotions in order to break free from the Promise. The Promise teaches us to operate from our heads, which often means we dismiss, avoid, or even detest our emotions. Now, that may not be true in every situation. We want to feel happy on Christmas morning when the kids are opening their gifts that we wrapped so dutifully at 1:00 a.m. And we don't want to feel angry at our kids when we've asked them three times to unload the dishwasher.

A few months ago, I was sharing with my husband how pissed off I was at something. I honestly can't remember what. His response was, "There is no use in getting angry about it. Anger won't help." Women aren't the only ones conditioned to push away how they feel. We live in a society where we've trained ourselves to show only what's acceptable or cover everything up and pretend we're fine. I don't know about you, but my family rarely modeled what it was like to acknowledge, accept, and process difficult emotions. We favored moving forward by keeping busy.

When I work with my clients to help them start to feel, it's often unfamiliar territory. First, for people who like being really good at things, feeling feelings is foreign and unpredictable. They don't know what will happen when they let their anger emerge. When they start to feel, will that feeling last forever? Or worse, will it get more intense and uncomfortable with time? The great news is that emotions don't stick around when we allow ourselves to be with them. According to neuroanatomist Dr. Jill Bolte Taylor, emotional reactions take only ninety seconds to process through the body.[37] I can attest to Dr. Taylor's findings. When I'm willing to feel my feelings, they rise and then dissipate quickly.

It's common to confuse feeling your feelings with reacting to them. When I'd get angry and turn into a screaming lunatic, I was reacting to a situation. I wasn't fully feeling the sensations in my body. When we give ourselves the space to feel, we naturally have an opportunity to choose how we want to react to a situation with more awareness and intention.

Allowing all emotions is like having a life experience that is rich, deep, and colorful, like a collage with such vibrancy you can't look away. Each piece draws you in, and you want to explore it fully.

Before you even entertain the idea of being with your feelings, it's important to not judge feelings. All feelings are valid and acceptable. When we judge how we feel, we naturally want to push that feeling away. Of course, you don't like being angry, anxious, or stressed, but each feeling is reasonable no matter what's happening in our lives.

To stop judging feelings, consider what it means to be a person with that unwanted feeling. The challenge is that we have ideas of what it means to be a stressed-out or angry person. Judging our feelings has been the way we've accommodated the Promise in our lives. It's been a survival tactic.

Being with the physical sensation without needing to label or judge the associated feeling may be the most accessible way for you to start to feel. After my dog Lexi passed away, I spent most of the day crying and enveloped in a fog. Grief had me feeling somber. I had to do mindless activities because my mind didn't have the capacity for much more. I noticed the heaviness on my shoulders and in my heart. For days, I just kept scanning and connecting with my body so that I could process my sadness.

The Promise tells us to not share our thoughts and feelings, to stay in line, and to be good. Being angry isn't quiet. And bawling doesn't show the world that we have our shit together, it shows the world we're falling apart. That's why feeling is so important. It's our expression that we've been tempering.

Getting to know how we really feel allows us to notice the impact of dieting and proving. It's an essential step in disconnecting from the Promise. Without allowing our emotions, we feel dulled. When we work so hard to mute ourselves, we create excessive tension and pressure in our bodies. Be willing and open. Let your emotions give you more information about who you truly are.

EXERCISE

Now that you're not judging your feelings, you're ready to feel them. Feelings aren't something we think about; they are what we feel inside our bodies.

Scan your body from head to toe noticing physical sensations.

This is information. You can name that sensation as an emotion, but you don't have to.

Give yourself a few moments to just be with the sensation you notice. Observe the pressure in your chest as simply pressure. If there is heat in your throat, just notice and be with that heat.

You may notice that the sensation moves or changes with time and your awareness.

That's all! Being present to the physical sensation of an emotion removes the internal drama around it.

LETTING YOURSELF CRY EVERY DAY

One way we feel our emotions is by giving ourselves permission to cry. As I started to be okay with my emotions, I began looking for dormant feelings I'd bottled inside. One day my energy instructor, Ava, suggested that I cry. Every day. Her instructions felt like a divine gift. I had needed someone to speak it out loud.

That day, I drove home from yoga and thought, *It's a good time to cry.* My car could be my cocoon, protecting me from anyone witnessing my tears. But only a few tears came. They were shy. Trying to cry felt foreign. I thought about actresses needing to manufacture emotion. Even if our expression conveys emotion, tears are the true indicator that our body contains emotions it needs to release. So instead of forcing myself to cry more, I yawned, trying to pull in more air into my lungs. This made sense to me—my lungs were filled with grief, and they were eager to release what I had not yet processed. I was giving my body permission to express herself.

A few days later, I sat at my desk working when a wave of sensation came over me and the tears just fell. Later that week, I watched a video of a news anchor interviewing the parents of a child who'd rushed a school shooter.

Their child was shot and died trying to save the lives of his classmates. I felt just a minuscule fraction of their pain, and there was no holding back my tears.

After the tears finished falling a few moments later, I felt relief. Like a weight had been lifted from my body. It wasn't a light and airy sensation; it felt soft and grounded. As if holding in the tears took effort and letting them go released tension.

In the past, I feared my tears. I had a vision of a gushing faucet. If it got turned on, I feared it would never shut off. How could I welcome an uncontrollable shit show? When I imagined myself crying, I saw myself curled up in a ball with the covers over my head.

But that's not what happened. Crying, like releasing any emotion, is a practice. We've gotten out of practice, and we need to remind ourselves that it's okay to do it. You don't need to be sad to cry, and crying doesn't mean you're going to slip into a deep depression, but please prioritize your mental health while you practice this exercise. If it doesn't feel right to you now, don't do it. As you disconnect from the Promise, you'll discover that you can trust your feelings and how your body processes emotions.

You've got some stored-up emotions that could use some discharging. I know this because we all do. Practice this exercise to help release them. If you're feeling stuck in some area of your life, that's a sign you're holding something in. If this exercise feels overwhelming because of a trauma or significant loss in your life, do it with the support of a therapist or coach. You may find that you like the release that comes from crying. You could do this exercise a few times a week or a few times a month.

EXERCISE

To let yourself cry, find a safe, quiet, undisturbed space. Set a timer for five to ten minutes. Let your body know that you're going to let it express its sadness and frustration.

You can think about a painful, unresolved memory. You can play a song that always moves you. Or you can just start to act like you're crying, like you're retraining your body how to release tears.

There is no right way to express emotion. The tears may fall or they may not. Celebrate yourself for giving yourself the time and space to feel.

BEFRIENDING YOUR CRITICAL INNER VOICE

Our critical inner voice is part of the human condition. Perhaps like yours, mine is deceptive. There was a time when I didn't notice the voice was critical. She says, "You can do better, Tara." Although this sounds like motivation, it's really dissatisfaction. No matter what I did, it was never good enough.

This voice is the result of internalizing the Promise. We don't need to hear other people's judgment of us because our inner voice judges us more harshly than anyone else. You may not notice your critical inner voice. Or she may scream so loudly that you can't imagine life without her. She's familiar. You also may believe that your voice is telling you the truth.

One of the common ways we've learned to deal with this critical inner voice is to treat her like an enemy. You've been told this voice is why you have low self-esteem and wonder if something is fundamentally wrong with you. This voice is the rebel, the resistor, and the pacifier, and you wish she didn't exist. If you could get rid of her, maybe all your problems would be solved.

But when does fighting against ourselves ever work? This is how the Promise is designed, for us to get in our own way pursuing something we can never attain. Your inner voice isn't the enemy; she was installed within you at a critical time in your life to keep you safe from danger. That voice wants to feel cute and special. She wants you to sit at the top, receive praise, be liked, be wanted. And she's using fear to get you there.

As you disconnect from the Promise, you're going to stop fighting yourself. This voice inside you just wants to be heard.

She's a part of you, and that doesn't mean she needs to continue to say what she says. Her words can evolve over time. The cruel words don't have to have any power over you when you realize they don't mean anything.

I don't hate that voice now. When she tells me I can do better, I respond, *Tell me what you are protecting me from. Tell me what you are afraid of. What are you hearing and seeing that I'm unwilling to look at?*

I don't need to fear this voice because I know she can't make me feel a certain way, act a certain way, and believe lies about myself. When I hear the voice for what she is, I invite her in and wrap my arms around her, and she loses any ability to take over. When I feared her, I denied a part of myself.

Befriending your inner voice is one of the ways you'll be defying the Promise. Fighting her can only hurt you and leave you feeling disconnected.

EXERCISE

Witness your inner voice. Get curious about her. Listen to her like you're sitting down with her for coffee.

It will be helpful to write down exactly what you hear

in your head. Our critical inner voice can often run like a tape that repeats itself over and over. You may be so familiar with the voice that you've stopped paying attention to the words you've been saying to yourself. Putting the words on paper helps you stop the tape and witness them.

As you become aware of this voice, you can intentionally choose positive thoughts.

You can ask yourself, *Is this a loving thought? Is this a helpful thought? Is this a thought that aligns with my values?* When you start to choose your thoughts, you will recognize how you have everything you need already … right inside you.

MOURNING THE PRICE YOU'VE PAID

What has the Promise cost you? It's time to get very clear on the price you've paid. What has it been like for you to diet and prove yourself? Are you angry? Get angry. No, scratch that. Get really pissed off. You have every right to. We've been duped. Being aware of the price you've paid is your insurance policy that you'll stop engaging in the Promise.

My friend Angella shared her wedding story on my podcast. All she could worry about was the rolls of skin under her armpits that were sticking out from her wedding dress. She reflected on this with deep remorse. She won't have another wedding day. She wonders how much more joy and celebration she could have felt on such a special day if she hadn't worried about her body.

In golf, when your ball barely leaves the tee or lands in the woods, you can hit it again. It's called a mulligan. But in life, we don't get a do-over. We've all been paying a big price by committing to the Promise. And we've done it willingly, expecting that the price we've paid would have a payoff. Now you know there will never, ever be a payoff. Angella didn't feel happier on her wedding day by being frustrated with her body.

When I think back to all the time and energy I spent trying to lose weight, obsessing over what I was going to eat, calorie counting, and willingly taking on every other task and chore in hopes it would change my body, I'm filled with regret, sadness, and anger. How about perfectionism? Everything I did was never enough. Any feeling of accomplishment never lasted long. It was exhausting. I held myself back because it was the safe thing to do. I was worried. I was stressed. I was preoccupied.

EXERCISE

What price have you paid to fulfill the Promise?

Consider all the people in your life. What has it been like for you to not fully share yourself? What is it like for your loved ones to not know the real you?

Now that you've acknowledged what the Promise has cost you, you can feel the sadness. Not just for the wasted time, but also for the dreams you held on to that will never be realized. To experience the sadness in your body, revisit the Feeling Your Emotions section in this chapter.

Recognize the price of false hope. Notice the part of you that loves feeling hopeful in a better version of yourself and a better life. You thought you could diet and prove yourself, and now you know you can't. Let yourself grieve. With time and compassion, you can let this part of you go.

Now you can begin to discover new hopes and dreams. Ones that aren't built on false safety and promises. Your dreams speak to you because they are yours, not someone else's.

BEING OKAY WITH DISCOMFORT

If you were to write your name with your nondominant hand, it would feel odd. Give it a try. Did you notice how sloppy and illegible your name looks? Or did you say to yourself, *I don't need to try that—I'll just keep reading.*

The Promise has conditioned us to do things well and show the world a perfect version of ourselves. We don't know how to suck at something. Now we know that being perfect is just a safety blanket, a blanket we no longer need. Coming out from under this safety blanket is uncomfortable. Just like writing with your opposite hand or picking up the pen in the first place.

Allow yourself to show up and not be great at something. Will you prioritize the playfulness that comes from trying something for the first time over needing to look good?

One evening I was teaching the side crow pose to my yoga class. I saw that some of my students weren't willing to even try the pose. They were more content to just watch others try. I asked, "What part of this pose is so hard?" "I'm afraid of falling," a few people said. My joke that the hospital was right around the corner only made them smile. My second joke, that their face wasn't far from the floor, still didn't help.

But I don't think they were really worried about breaking their nose or bruising their cheek; they were more worried about looking bad. They didn't want to be the one student in class who couldn't do the pose.

Whether you're unwilling to try or are determined to be perfect, these motivations have the same origin. As you break yourself from the Promise, changing your approach to every task will feel foreign. It will feel like you're doing it wrong. You may hear that little voice inside you saying, *You're being lazy, You can do better than this,* or *Don't embarrass yourself.*

A few years ago when I wanted to try something new, I took singing lessons. Part of me wanted to heal from that incredibly embarrassing moment in middle school chorus when the teacher made us sing in front of everyone. I barely sang above a whisper. After a few private lessons, I realized I'm not that interested in singing. And that's okay—what mattered is that I tried something knowing I didn't have to be perfect at it.

EXERCISE

Practice letting yourself suck. This includes being uncomfortable with things not being done the way you do them. You don't have to control everything. Start with small tasks and projects that don't feel important to you.

Consider all the tasks that you automatically do and *need* to do. What if you chose to not do them? You could leave the kitchen sink filled with dishes and go to bed. You could ask your partner or teenager to go to the grocery store for you, even if they bring home the "wrong" toilet paper. You could do your own laundry and tell the other capable adults and teenagers in your home to do their own. When your mother calls and you're in the middle of something or don't want to speak with her, don't.

Be okay with what I call a "B-". This is my favorite way of doing necessary tasks and projects in my business without needing to do them perfectly. I'll write a newsletter or a piece of content and let myself send it to the world without laboring over it for hours. I'll drop a podcast with no editing. I'll only allow myself one or two attempts at a reel and share it because it's good enough.

This will get easier over time. And you'll find that you're going to save yourself a lot of time and energy while you're practicing it.

SWIMMING UPSTREAM

You haven't recognized the Promise as a problem until now because everyone around you is also fulfilling it. No one is calling out your perfectionistic tendencies because they are operating in the same way or they are benefiting from it. You haven't seen dieting as a problem because you may have watched your mother diet or you may have joined Weight Watchers when your employer sponsored the program at work.

Fulfilling the Promise is going with the flow. As you start detaching from the Promise, it can feel like you're swimming upstream against all the fish swimming downstream. And just yesterday, you were one of those fish! You swam downstream, not challenging the Promise like you're willing to do today.

No longer dieting—in fact, *rejecting* dieting— means you're going to step outside the familiar circles that have been intact. What do you talk about to other people? What do you have in common with them? You may be worried that you'll lose certain relationships when you no longer share the struggles and challenges that have tied you together for so long. Not only that, but when you stop dieting, people may worry about you or think you're crazy. "Aren't you invested in your health?" they may ask or insinuate. When you stop dieting, you may also make others question their own dieting practices which may make them feel uncomfortable.

It also means that the people in your life will be seeing a different version of you. Those close to you may treat you as if you have changed your political affiliation. "What have you done with the woman I know and love?" they may ask. "Who are you?" Your loved ones will notice when you stop fulfilling the Promise. Mine did when I started to eat certain foods guilt-free. I stopped bringing my own food everywhere I went and started to allow myself to eat the food available to me.

This can feel like a lot to handle. Go slowly. Disconnecting from the Promise doesn't need to be traumatic. I didn't cannonball into the intuitive eating deep end. Not even close. I did it the way I step into New Hampshire's frigid Atlantic ocean in early summer: I walk in slowly, often holding my breath. Making my way to my waist and then stopping. Just like in the ocean, it took me many contemplative moments before I dunked. Sometimes, it was more like putting my big toe in the cold water and then running to the comfort of my soft beach towel.

I still tried the keto diet after practicing intuitive eating for years. I even engaged in some autoimmune "solutions" that had me monitoring my blood sugar. The lure of dieting enticed me, even when I knew it wouldn't work. Part of me just needed more evidence to be sure. Swimming upstream can be challenging; it can often feel like you're taking five steps forward and twenty-seven steps back.

I still see my patterns of pursuing perfectionism, and as many of these patterns that I've dismantled, there are just as many that still live and breathe within me. Damn. I know how challenging this is. Yet the more I practice, the easier it gets.

EXERCISE

Reflect on a time when you've done something that no one else around you has done. Maybe you were a kid and wanted to sit in the front of the class when the rest of your friends sat in the back. Or you wanted to take an art class, even though you didn't know anyone who had ever done art. Chances are, you've been swimming upstream your whole life. Now it's time to recognize the truth within you.

Get out your journal and start to explore this in writing.

What does it feel like to trust yourself and your inner wisdom? Be curious and notice that sensation inside you.

It can feel harder to swim upstream when you're running low on resilience and inner clarity. This happens when you feel run down and depleted.

How can you care for yourself in order to strengthen your inner resources?

Creating a morning routine with time for stillness, reflection, prayer, and movement is a great way to keep your resilience up. You don't need to spend an hour or two. Finding ten to twenty minutes in the morning can have a big impact.

CREATING NEW COMMUNITY

You're likely familiar with the infamous quote from the movie *Fight Club*: "The first rule of fight club is you do not talk about fight club." When we don't talk about something, especially when we are trying to cover up something, our stories and experiences stay hidden. This is certainly true when it comes to the psychological consequences we suffer when trying to fulfill the Promise. Perfectionism and dieting have been so normalized that we don't talk about their inevitable side effect: feeling like a failure. When we don't talk about this with full transparency, we stay engaged in the Promise. And when we keep quiet, we feel alone and disconnected, which only leads to self-blame.

To break the Promise, we need to break the first rule of fight club. We need to start sharing what the Promise is and what it's really doing to us. By sharing our stories and hearing them from other women, we won't feel so alone. Because you now have a name for what you've been experiencing, you can share what the Promise is with your loved ones. You can tell them that the Promise is designed for us to fail. And that it's designed to keep us engaged in it.

I was on a small group mastermind call recently when I began to cry. I shared how my striving was leaving me exhausted. Letting each of my colleagues and collaborators see me was a relief. I felt raw, but lighter. I had shed another layer of myself, another part of me that was conditioned to fulfill the Promise. Over the years, I've gotten good at knowing who I want to surround myself with. I've also allowed myself to share myself more fully.

The journey you're about to embark on goes deep. You're not just trying to change some unwanted habits. You're exploring and discovering yourself without the expectations that have been imposed on you since your first breath. I will share more on this in chapter 7. In the meantime, welcome to this exploration of yourself.

EXERCISE

Reach out to someone you trust deeply. Share with them what you've discovered for yourself.

Gather a group of women and read this book in your book club. Or create your own book club and start with this book.

Share your story and be a willing witness to theirs.

You likely noticed that I didn't give you a playbook. I am not offering you a new set of rules to follow. I am only offering you the practices that will bring you back to yourself. Giving you a playbook would just be replacing the Promise with another set of rules to follow. I can't tell you how to be yourself—no one can.

Unlike the Promise, which starts and ends by what's happening on the *outside*, success lives on the *inside*. What we look like, how large our body is, and what foods we are eating is how we show the world a put-together, perfect version of ourselves. The only way to experience true success is to stand in your own light, where you can acknowledge, respect, and celebrate yourself.

CHAPTER 7

YOUR NEW ADVENTURE

We were born into the Promise of the Thin and Perfect, but we were also born with a unique fire that lives inside. You may or may not have glimpsed this fire sometime in your life, but now it's time to reclaim it and stoke it back to a blaze.

When holding a newborn, you can appreciate what it feels like to hold a divine blessing and gift. When each of my three children were born, I was overwhelmed by their magnificence and the magic that brought them into the world. Along with our essence, we have within us the resilience, gifts, doubts, fears, and everything else that makes us human. There is no doubt that we are perfect, although not in terms of achieving a standard someone else has set for us, but in the way that our unique being is perfect. We are whole and complete because we have everything inside that we could want or need. We're not missing anything. There is nothing inside us that needs fixing. The magnificence we witness in a newborn lives within us.

It's time for an internal rebellion. It may be subtle—we aren't marching the Capitol or in our local cities with signs that say "No More Promises" (although that's not a bad idea). We are giving up and letting go to enrich our lives. With each small choice—to take a nap, to eat foods we love, to take a lovely walk with a friend instead of pounding it out on the Peloton, to see our body as something that doesn't need to be fixed—we liberate ourselves. We break free.

It's time to create a new promise with yourself. Now that you have the guidance on how to break free from the Promise, you can create something new. You get to choose how you want to authentically live.

You're stepping away from the Promise and stepping toward your brilliance.

Take a moment and reflect on how you know your brilliance lives inside you.

How has it been shown to you? Was there a time in your life when you were so indisputably *you* that no one could have convinced you to act otherwise? You may have been playful, you may have been outspoken, or you may have seen what others couldn't see. If nothing comes to mind, let yourself imagine your true and highest self. What does she think? How does she feel? What lights her up?

She's there and you're going to be experiencing and knowing even more of her. You may be eager for an instruction guide or a checklist to follow, but as I said, I'm not going to offer you that. I'm not an expert on you or the new promise you want to make. What I will be sharing with you are ways to create this promise so it feels aligned and true to you. You're free to design and follow through on your unique and brilliant promise on your terms.

FOLLOWING YOUR PASSION: MY STORY

The closer I got to knowing myself and connecting to my body, the clearer my passions and the vision of my work became. I was no longer distracted by stepping on the scale or worrying that I just ate a second helping of pasta. I made my big leap out of accounting and into full-time coaching in 2019. Had I been consumed with weight loss, I never would have had the mental and emotional resiliency to take such a risk. In my accounting business, spreadsheets were comfortable and safe. I was also guilty of convincing myself that I didn't need to do passionate work. It was okay that I felt accomplished. I was hoping that my bank account and the money I made in my consulting business were enough to make me happy. The Promise has a way of convincing us that money defines our success.

I'm happy to report that I'm no longer running three businesses. Some of the changes happened because I made them happen, and some changes were outside my control. I closed my yoga studio when my landlord told me he wouldn't be renewing my lease. Honestly, it was a blessing. But it was painful. Closing those doors shook a lot of things up, mostly with my relationships. I was relieved to have only two businesses to run, but I felt like I was working full time in both without moving either one forward. It took me a full year to realize this one thing: I needed to give myself permission to be happy and pursue work I felt deep passion for.

This meant dropping a mask I had created for myself. I believed that as a CPA and an accountant, I was working in a more esteemed industry. I was proud of my career, but when I was attached to it as an identity, I realized that it wasn't the real me, it was just me showing the world a smart and professional version of myself. The real me felt deeply passionate about women struggling with food and body image. This was one of the ways the Promise was holding me back—by insisting I do more and do more "professionally acceptable" work to look good and prove my worth.

I had to let go of myself and give myself permission to be myself at the same time. I also had to recognize the value in my own message and approach. My coaching business doesn't fit into traditional constructs. It can often be challenging to explain and is often misunderstood. As I mentioned before, I'm viewing the world differently from the majority opinion, so I feel like I'm swimming upstream. This can feel lonely at times.

Please don't get the impression that this was a seamless, easy process. There were times when I feared failure and wondered if I was crazy. Why did I leave a business that was so easy to run and grow? Along this new path, I've questioned and doubted myself. I've grown personally and professionally. But one thing that keeps me going is my passion to make a difference in people's lives. I know I can't fail at pursuing what I love. Failing is only the construct of the Promise.

But it's the conditioning of the Promise that tells me I need external validation to feel good about myself and the work I'm sharing in the world. Letting go of my accounting business was a huge way that I let go of this need. Now, I can feel my business inside me. My energy offers me insight, and my body shares with me her wisdom. Just like I would feel exhausted by doing accounting work, I felt a surge of energy and passion when working with coaching clients, writing content and books, and interviewing for my podcast. By letting go of the Promise inside me, I was able to share myself more and more.

I remind myself regularly that there is no perfect way for me to be me. In fact, by definition, whatever I'm doing, it is perfect. I often choose to allow you to see an "imperfect" version of me. I'd rather you see my true journey than no journey at all.

You may have a business you're passionate about. You may work with a nonprofit you're jazzed and energized by. You may have children or grandchildren that you love focusing your time and energy on. No matter what or who, know what you stand for. Connect with your passion and purpose. This will put your old way of living at odds with what you want to create.

You'll need to redefine success for yourself, as I did. For me, it was no longer about doing the right thing, being perfect, and building a business that looked a certain way. It has been my work in progress. I've created a business on my own terms, in a way that's aligned with me. My business has been the mechanism I've used to create my new promise to myself.

As you connect with your true self even more, it's her that you'll be trusting. We've been told to trust the authority figures in our lives: physicians, coaches, teachers, parents. We've been encouraged to follow their guidance—often without any consideration for the guidance that lives inside us.

Bring along faith in yourself as you create this new promise, and trust will follow.

PRACTICING BEGINNER'S MIND

In yoga philosophy, the concept of the beginner's mind is powerful. When newbies came into my yoga studio, I felt giddy and honored to be in the presence of someone who had no idea what the hell they were doing. With a beginner's mind, a new yoga student can be curious, awestruck, and excited about their experience. They can tune in to all the subtleties of a pose, because their burning quads in chair pose or their tight hamstrings in down dog is a new sensation.

When we practice being in a beginner's mind, whether we're doing something for the first time or the hundred thousandth, everything is fresh and sharp. When you moved into your home, I'm sure you noticed every detail—for example, the color of your neighbor's door, the beautiful birch tree along the side of the road, and the way the sun shadows the road during a certain time of day. You had a beginner's mind. But over time, your attention to these details has faded. Now, you can drive home in your sleep because you've done it so often.

After you've finished reading this book, your life is

going to look the same way it did before you knew about the Promise. You will have the same job, home, relationships, bank account and body. But now that you're creating a new promise, you need to view your life with fresh eyes.

The beginner's mind offers you an approach to the same tasks you've been doing in your life with a new awareness. This will be challenging at first because it takes effort. You're turning your senses on while living through familiar experiences. As a result, the familiar may feel fresh and raw. The cool thing about the beginner's mind is when you start to notice your internal experience like it's new, you'll have information and guidance around what feels, tastes, sounds, and smells good to you, and what doesn't.

I encourage clients to bring their beginner's mind when eating certain foods. Do those Oreos taste as good to you as you remember? You've been eating salads for lunch every day—do they taste as good and leave you as content as you'd like? When your boss asks you for something with an unrealistic deadline and you notice yourself wanting to say yes, what else do you notice? Do you notice the sensation of overwhelm and the relief of pleasing someone else, all at the same time?

Your beginner's mind is a crucial practice to designing your new promise. It's how you're waking yourself up and noticing how it feels to navigate parts of your life on your own terms. Be curious. Ask yourself lots of questions. And imagine you're being introduced to your life for the first time. Because you are.

GIVING YOURSELF PERMISSION

When we follow someone else's rules, we often forget that we have the power to do one thing: choose something different. To make a new choice, we need to be willing to explore new territory. I think of this as giving yourself permission. There are plenty of things you can give yourself permission to do. Let's explore some critical areas.

▪ CREATE YOUR OWN RULES

In my podcast interview with Kelly Diels, feminist marketer and writer, she shared the moment she realized that dieting was a cultural norm created to make women small, literally and figuratively. It was a life-altering moment for Kelly. She stopped dieting on the spot. And then Kelly did something equally brilliant. She asked a dietician friend to teach her how to eat again.

Kelly had been following dieting rules for decades. Just like me, and likely you, she thought she was doing the right thing. The moment she realized dieting wasn't right for her and her values, she no longer needed the diet's rules. She was going to create her own.

No one is going to give you permission to design a new promise. You're the only one who can do that. Your own rules start with what you value and what's important to you. You get to know inside what success feels like, which means you start with your inner compass.

▪ DO NOT LOVE OR HATE YOUR BODY

I'll state the obvious. We all have a body. We didn't get to choose the body we were born with. Thanks to the genetics from our biological parents, we get what we get.

Even though you may agree with me that you don't get to have a different body, I understand that loving your body may feel impossible. At the moment. Which is why it's important to give yourself permission to not *love* your body.

Giving yourself permission to *not* love your body is giving yourself permission to grieve the fantasy you've invested in with the Promise. Remember the grieving you did back in chapter 6? You were hoping your life would be amazing by fulfilling the Promise, but your life is the same as it was yesterday. Trying to be perfect and thin isn't going to give you that amazing life. That's a lot to be sad and angry about. Give yourself space to feel that despair.

Even though you don't have to love your body, you are still the only person who's responsible for caring for it. This isn't a job you can outsource, nor do you want to. You're the person who chooses how to nourish yourself, how much sleep you get, and when you seek health care.

▪ NEED WHAT YOU NEED

Just like our need for rest and nourishment makes us human, our emotions also make us human. When you start to tune in to your body, you'll start to notice feelings. I shared in chapter 6 how to be with your feelings, process them, and most importantly, not judge them. One of the biggest challenges I hear from clients about their feelings is whether they are valid. These women may notice a feeling but immediately negotiate with it and wonder, *Is it okay to feel that? Why do I feel that?*

What needs do you have around your health, your body, and your own healing journey? When you're free from the Promise, consider your personal values. As I mentioned before, we've been duped into believing our worth is wrapped up in our bodies and our ability to be perfect. Aren't we so much more than that? What needs do we have that aren't being met?

Now that you're designing a new promise with yourself, start with two basic assumptions. Repeat them after me: *I have needs that deserve to be met. I have feelings that are valid and deserve to be felt.* To help you internalize this, I highly recommend the Nonviolent

Communication[38] approach, built on the principle that behind every unmet need is a painful emotion. When we allow ourselves to acknowledge our needs, we can find a thousand strategies to meet them. When our needs are met, our feelings change. Practicing compassion with yourself, something you've been depriving yourself of in the past, is going to be a crucial practice for you moving forward.

▪ FEEL GIDDY

Consider what it would be like to surround yourself with things you love that make you feel great. For so many of us, our closets can feel complicated, overwhelming, and a source of discontentment. When I was juggling my yoga studio and accounting business, I wore yoga pants and mala beads some days and button-up dress tops with heels on other days. I was wearing what I thought I should be wearing, things I liked enough. But I rarely felt at home in my clothes because they were not a reflection of me.

After all, how could I dress myself when I hadn't given myself permission to know myself and find those clothes that felt giddy and juicy to me? I started to pay attention to how my body felt when I was in my closet. My body felt heavy, which I realized was part overwhelm and part dread.

By tuning in to the inside instead of looking on the outside for the right things to wear, I've slowly been able to discover what clothes, styles, and colors I love to wear. This isn't about valuing material possessions and having an Instagram-worthy closet. Every human needs to wear clothing. Choosing clothing that we can afford and, more important, that feels right is a step toward honoring ourselves.

Do you know yourself? Do you know what pieces of clothing make your body light up? What sweater you can't wait to put on? What fabric you love because it feels so incredible on your skin? What color warms your heart? Or have you been settling for the life you have and the material possessions you once thought you should have?

As you engage in this new promise, the one that is aligned with who you are, those things you add or remove in your life are an expression of you.

If you're feeling lost around this, take a moment to ask your body what a "yes" feels like. Remember the exercise from Living in Your Body in chapter 6? It may help to bring into mind your dream vacation or a favorite memory with a loved one. How did your body tell you that that situation was a yes? I often notice a lightness and even some warm energy, almost as if something has been ignited in me.

Now consider what a "no" feels like. You can just say the word "no" to yourself or bring in a memory or object you don't like. When I do this, my body often slumps, and I can feel a weight on my shoulders. It's amazing how your body offers you guidance. Let it guide you to design your life so that all that is around you and inside you is a reflection of you. You deserve to surround yourself with things, people, and experiences that make you feel giddy. You're worth it.

▪ TRUST YOURSELF

As you create your promise, the one that's aligned with who you are and what you value, healing your nervous system will take some practice and awareness. Sadly, we are just too accustomed to feeling overwhelmed, frustrated, numb, and disconnected. Your body is a resource, and a calm nervous system is a system you can trust.

Start by getting to know what being grounded and present feels like in your body. It may take only a few moments to shift into a present state. It can be as simple as taking some deep breaths or visualizing your feet anchored to the ground. Taking note of when you're activated is equally important. You can't shift what you don't notice.

While you're befriending your nervous system, start to change your expectations as a mother, wife, woman, executive, business owner, daughter, and sister. Perfectionism limits new possibilities from coming into your life. Now that you're no longer buying into the Promise, expanding what kind of choices you make around work and family responsibilities allows you to have more space for your own well-being. When you start to open up your options, that's when real freedom enters.

You don't need to attend every meeting you get invited to. You don't need to promise deliverables at the earliest possible time. You don't need to respond to every email and text within a certain period of time. Give yourself plenty of breathing room. Allow yourself tech-free days every week. And of course, please stop trying to fix your body. Dieting is a way of fighting against your body and fleeing the present moment.

When you engage in ways to support your body so you can feel safe, something magical will happen. You'll feel more creative and expansive. You'll naturally engage in the world around you with great curiosity, because your internal state is safe for connection.

Have you ever had a moment when you just knew that all was well? These don't need to be joyful moments, like on Christmas morning or at the start of a long-awaited tropical beach vacation. These are moments when you can feel deep in your belly that you are exactly where you need to be. You may feel peaceful and relaxed but not necessarily blissed out like you've had an hour-long massage. Your senses are alive, and you're tuned in to the moment. If you've had these moments and have them often, you know how priceless they are. As you create and live out a new promise for yourself, you'll have more and more of these moments.

As you start to live with a new promise, you'll be liberated to reclaim your time and energy. You don't need to be pursuing anything else. In fact, you can do *one* thing that will make a remarkable difference for you: be present. When you practice being in the present moment, feeling it, noticing what's happening around you, checking in with your body, and enjoying it, so much of your life will shift. You'll see that the present moment is all you really need. And you'll know that all is well.

SHARING YOUR BRILLIANCE

Our new promise to ourselves is a freakin' adventure and an internal revolution. It takes time to replace those painful patterns with ones that fill us with nourishment and vitality. You may not have the excitement and enthusiasm from a new adventure just yet, but it's coming. Let the overthrow happen internally, replacing all patterns with new ones. Untether yourself from the Promise that our happiness and success needs to be defined by how we look and how happy we make those around us.

When you start fulfilling your newly designed promise, you'll be living with integrity and authenticity. Instead of pleasing and pretending, your life will feel authentic to you. Integrity to me looks like saying what I believe, without trying to hide it out of fear of judgment or ridicule. It looks like setting boundaries that support my well-being instead of doing backflips for clients like I often did when I was running my accounting business. Fulfilling this new promise is a practice that never ends. You'll never arrive at some declared place, but you'll know when you start to feel truly seen.

You'll start to trust yourself. You'll have more space in your mind and in your life. Living inside your body is going to bring you great confidence and ultimate freedom. I'm humbled by my journey with my body, and it continues to take me deeper. On your adventure, curiosity will be your favorite way of navigating life. Keep asking questions. Be in a state of wonder. After all, you're free now.

I don't know where your adventure of sharing your brilliance will take you, but I'm so excited for you. Will you share your adventures with me by emailing me at hello@tara-whitney.com? My wish for you is that by getting to know yourself, you'll allow the world to see you just as you are. This is the greatest gift you can offer yourself and the world. Your true expression is your most vibrant self. The world needs to see the true, untethered you. Your loved ones want to connect with the authentic you. Your business wants the real you.

As you connect with your true expression and allow yourself to be truly seen, you're going to light up your life. That's a promise you can fulfill.

ENDNOTES

1. Elizabeth Yuko, "13 Women CEOs Who Made History," Reader's Digest, 10, https://www.rd.com/list/women-ceos-who-made-history/.

2. Rebecca Winke, "History of Female Property Rights and Ownership," last modified November 22, 2021, https://www.familyhandyman.com/article/women-property-rights-history/.

3. "15 Everyday Things Women Could Not Do in the Past," Pulpastic, last modified July 4, 2022, https://pulptastic.com/when-could-women/.

4. "The Simple Truth About the Gender Pay Gap: 2021 Update," AAUW, 3, https://www.aauw.org/app/uploads/2021/09/AAUW_SimpleTruth_2021_-fall_update.pdf.

5. P. Roehling, M. Roehling, J. Vandlen, J. Blazek, and W. Guy, "Weight Discrimination and the Glass Ceiling Effect Among Top US CEOs," Equal Opportunities International 28, no. 2 (2009): 179–96, https://doi.org/10.1108/02610150910937916.

6. C. D. Fryar, M. D. Carroll, and J. Afful, "Prevalence of Overweight, Obesity, and Severe Obesity Among Adults Aged 20 and Over: United States, 1960–1962 Through 2017–2018," Centers for Disease Control and Prevention, NCHS Health E-Stats,

7. D. Crystal and S. Dunn, "Average American Women's Clothing Size: Comparing National Health and Nutritional Examination Surveys (1988–2010) to ASTM International Misses & Women's Plus Size Clothing," International Journal of Fashion Design, Technology and

Education 10, no. 2 (August 2016): 129–36, https://doi.org/10.10
80/17543266.2016.1214291.

8. "The $72 Billion Weight Loss & Diet Control Market in the United
States, 2019-2023," Business Wire, February 25, 2019, https://
www.businesswire.com/news/home/20190225005455/en/
The-72-Billion-Weight-Loss-Diet-Control-Market-in-the-United-
States-2019-2023---Why-Meal-Replacements-are-Still-Booming-
but-Not-OTC-Diet-Pills---ResearchAndMarkets.com.

9. "Weight Watchers," Wikipedia, last modified November 17, 2022,
https://en.wikipedia.org/wiki/WW_International.

10. "Jenny Craig," Wikipedia, last modified August 22, 2022, https://
en.wikipedia.org/wiki/Jenny_Craig,_Inc.

11. "A Social and Cultural History of Smoking", Britannica, accessed
November 15, 2022, https://www.britannica.com/topic/smok-
ing-tobacco/A-social-and-cultural-history-of-smoking.

12. Remy Franklin, "11 Surprising Mobile Health Statistics," Mobius
MD, October 25, 2021, https://mobius.md/2021/10/25/11-mo-
bile-health-statistics/.

13. MyFitnessPal, accessed November 15,2022, https://www.myfitness-
pal.com/.

14. Megan Brenan, "Women Still Handle Main Household Tasks
in U.S.," Gallup, January 29, 2020, https://news.gallup.com/
poll/283979/women-handle-main-household-tasks.aspx.

15. Georgi Todorov, "27 Great Male vs Female CEO Stats [Revealing
Power Norms through CEO Stats]," ThriveMyWay, last modified October 17, 2022, https://thrivemyway.com/male-vs-female-ceo-stats/.

16. Carol Sharick, "Registration Now Open for the Global Leadership
Summit for Black Male Students," UMass Amherst College of Social
& Behavioral Sciences SBS Pathways Center, accessed February
1, 2022, https://sbspathways.umass.edu/blog/2022/02/01/
registration-now-open-for-the-global-leadership-summit-for-black-
male-students/.

17. Robby Berman, "Women Are More Productive Than Men, According to New Research," World Economic Forum, October 8, 2018,
https://www.weforum.org/agenda/2018/10/women-are-more-
productive-than-men-at-work-these-days.

18. Sky Ariella, "25 Women in Leadership Statistics [2022]: Facts on the Gender Gap in Corporate and Political Leadership," November 9, 2022, https://www.zippia.com/advice/women-in-leadership-statistics/.

19. Ragen Chastain, "Who Says Dieting Fails Most of the Time?," Substack, November 6, 2021, https://weightandhealthcare.substack.com/p/who-says-dieting-fails-the-majority?.

20. Jack Guy, "The More We Watch TV, the More We Prefer Thinner Female Bodies, Study Shows," CNN.com, December 19, 2019, https://www.cnn.com/2019/12/19/health/television-bodies-nica-ragua-scli-intl-scn-wellness.

21. Rebecca Puhl, "Weight Stigma Study in the U.S. and 5 Other Nations Shows the Worldwide Problem of Such Prejudice," Washington Post, June 12, 2021, https://www.washingtonpost.com/health/overweight-discrimination-common-harmful/2021/06/11/2946c538-c88c-11eb-afd0-9726f7ec0ba6_story.html.

22. Ronald Alsop, "Fat People Earn Less and Have a Harder Time Finding Work," BBC.com, December 1, 2016, https://www.bbc.com/worklife/article/20161130-fat-people-earn-less-and-have-a-harder-time-finding-work.

23. "Allostatic load," Wikipedia, last modified October 22, 2022, https://en.wikipedia.org/wiki/Allostatic_load.

24. Lindo Bacon, "Health at Every Size-Excerpts," accessed January 10, 2023, https://lindobacon.com/HAESbook/HAES_Understand-ingSetpoint_Bacon.pdf.

25. Evelyn Tribole, "Warning: Dieting Increases Your Risk of Gaining More Weight (An Update)," January 21, 2012, http://www.intuitiveeating.org/warning-dieting-increases-your-risk-of-gaining-more-weight-an-update/.

26. Chantal Gil, "The Starvation Experiment," DukeHealth, accessed January 11, 2023, https://eatingdisorders.dukehealth.org/educa-tion/resources/starvation-experiment.

27. Eric Stice, Jeff M. Gau, Paul Rohde, and Heather Shaw, "Risk Factors That Predict Future Onset of Each DSM-5 Eating Disorder: Predictive Specificity in High-Risk Adolescent Females," Journal of Abnormal Psychology 126, no. 1 (2017): 38–51, https://doi.org/10.1037/abn0000219.

28. Perfect Illusions: Eating Disorders and the Family, https://www.pbs.org/perfectillusions/eatingdisorders/preventing_facts.html.

29. Barbara Spanjers, "Eating Disorder Statistics: Get the Facts Here," Center For Discovery, accessed January 6, 2023, https://centerfordiscovery.com/blog/get-the-facts-eating-disorder-statistics/.

30. "Statistics & Research on Eating Disorders," National Eating Disorders Association, accessed January 7,2023, https://www.nationaleatingdisorders.org/statistics-research-eating-disorders.

31. Ragen Chastein, Dances With Fat, accessed January 11,2023, https://danceswithfat.org/.

32. "About Health at Every Size® (HAES®)," accessed January 11, 2022, https://asdah.org/health-at-every-size-haes-approach/.

33. Cristin D. Runfola, Ph.D., Ann Von Holle, M.S. Sara E. Trace, Ph.D.,Kimberly A. Brownley, Ph.D.,Sara M. Hofmeier, M.S., L.P.C.,Danielle A. Gagne, B.A.,and Cynthia M. Bulik, Ph.D., "Body Dissatisfaction in Women Across the Lifespan," European Eating Disorders Review 21, no. 1, https://www.ncbi.nlm.nih.gov/pmc/articles/PMC3745223/.

34. Andrew Lenderman, "Girls Who Code Founder Encourages Taking Risks, Fighting Perfectionism," Association of Washington Business, September 17, 2020, https://www.awb.org/girls-who-code-founder-encourages-taking-risks-fighting-perfectionism/.

35. Women's Summit 2019 (brochure), Bryant University, accessed January 12, 2023, https://wsummit.bryant.edu/archive/womens-summit-2019/.

36. Tara Sophia Mohr, "Why Women Don't Apply for Jobs Unless They're 100% Qualified," Harvard Business Review, August 25, 2014, https://hbr.org/2014/08/why-women-dont-apply-for-jobs-unless-theyre-100-qualified.

37. Bryan Robinson, "The 90-Second Rule That Builds Self-Control," Psychology Today, April 26, 2020, https://www.psychologytoday.com/us/blog/the-right-mindset/202004/the-90-second-rule-builds-self-control?eml.

38. https://www.nonviolentcommunication.com/

ACKNOWLEDGMENTS

This book is very personal to me. I was able to share as much of myself as I did because of these amazing people:

Thanks to my husband, Mark. Every time I doubted or questioned myself you would simply say "Tara, just be you." and "You've got this." And then gave me a big hug. You say what I need to hear 90% of the time :). That's enough for me.

Thanks to my kids; Ryan, Garrett and Anna. You've offered me some awesome advice and are always encouraging me in your own unique ways. I'm so blessed. You don't need to read this book. I love you no matter what.

Thank you, Amy Isaman. You are so much more than a book coach. You offered all the right encouragement and asked all the right questions. You're a gift.

This book wouldn't be possible without the expertise, creativity and diligence of Domini Dragoone, Christina Roth, Maggie Van Galen, and Holly Tomilson.

Thanks to my clients and colleagues for reminding me how important this work is and encouraging me to keep with it. Your words of support always came at the exact right time.

I leaned in often to the divine, loving spirit that lives within me and all around me, guiding me to share my own wisdom so I can make the world a better place. I'm deeply grateful.

ABOUT THE AUTHOR

Tara Whitney is a sought-after coach that helps women leaders and executives feel better about their bodies so they can be more effective professionally and personally. She draws upon her training with the Gestalt International Study Center, her certification as an intuitive eating counselor, her experience as a yoga teacher and Reiki master, and her extensive business and entrepreneurial background when working with her clients.

Her first book, *Hungry: Trust Your Body and Free Your Mind around Food,* offers a fresh perspective on why women have struggled with food and gives them a path to set themselves free. Tara lives on the Seacoast of New Hampshire.

Made in United States
North Haven, CT
03 April 2023

34975842R00102